Dad,

With very many happy returns
for the 6th,
with love from,

Ian, Liz, Colin & Fiona

6th April, '64.

THE GREAT WORKS OF MANKIND

A VISUAL HISTORY

This is the third volume in
the Bodley Head Visual History series.
The previous volumes were
EUROPE
100,000 YEARS OF DAILY LIFE

THE GREAT WORKS
OF MANKIND

A VISUAL HISTORY

by Jacques Boudet

Claude Manceron and Jacques Ostier

UNDER THE GENERAL EDITORSHIP OF

Robert Laffont

TRANSLATED BY

Anne Carter

THE BODLEY HEAD

LONDON

LES GRANDS TRAVAUX DE L'HUMANITÉ
(Paris 1961)

THE GREAT WORKS OF MANKIND
(London 1962)

Preface by Jules Moch

This is not a history book. Nor is it a straightforward picture book. It is designed on the lines of a film in which words and pictures are complementary.

Its subject is the great works of mankind, that is to say, man's modification of his physical surroundings, when the methods brought to this task have been more exceptional than those normal to the society of the time. The great works of man's spirit, whose effects are less tangibly perceptible, fall outside the scope of this survey.

The progress of civilisation has shown a tendency to spread across the globe from east to west. Taking its origin in the heart of Asia, cultural life spread from there to the Near East, the cradle of monotheism, and so, through Greece, into Europe. With the turn of the present century the New World, and North America in particular, began to take the lead in industrial development. Today Russia and China are emerging to dispute America's lead. The growth of scientific progress has swept in a full circle round the northern hemisphere within a few thousand years, while south of the Equator the world has begun its apprenticeship to modern industry.

What of the next few thousand years? We do not know. Myths apart, all these great works have been crowded into the seventy centuries or so of man's history, as we know it. But for how long has man been searching and striving?

To judge by the radio-activity in the soil, it is evident that the earth has supported life for thousands of millions of years. But it is only for tens of thousands of these that man has differed from the animals. For a long time he left no trace behind him but his own skeletons. The oldest human 'archives' are stone implements, and these are only about a hundred thousand years old; the first, rudimentary traces of man acting on his surroundings are barely seven thousand.

One comparison is sufficient to bring home to us the proportion of history to pre-history. If we suppose that a single step is equivalent to a thousand years, the history of life on earth would stretch roughly from the Urals to the Atlantic Ocean. Man's story covers only the last few hundred yards of this route. His first tools come within a hundred yards of the end and all his scientific discoveries together are crowded into the last fifteen feet. Within these few paces whole civilisations have sprung up, flourished and died away, leaving the evidence of their great works for those who come after them.

Human endeavour has been inspired in turn by faith, pride and prosperity. Faith raised lofty temples. The Pyramids, Notre Dame de Paris, the Wailing Wall, the Temples of Angkor and the Mosque of Cordova, all these edifices bear witness to fear of God and belief in an after life.

Pride, either of a single man or a whole society, demanded the building of castles to dominate other dwellings round about, of city ramparts and frontier walls.

Next, collective effort began to find people seeking better conditions and distractions. After her temples and palaces, Rome built arenas and drove her roads in straight lines across Europe. Today transport and communications enjoy a special priority, while palaces have been superseded by enormous schools, hospitals and industrial plants.

Civilisations develop at an ever-increasing rate. The rewards increase in proportion to technical developments, so that ten years of the nuclear age can be more productive than a century of steam or than a thousand years' reliance on the strength of the human arm.

Primitive man's only source of power lay in his own muscles. His first triumph came when he learned to adapt the elements of his work, reducing the effort required by distributing the burden. His task was made easier by ropes, levers, rollers and wheel-barrows. Next he increased his own capacities by harnessing nature; he tamed animals and invented the sail and the water-wheel to take advantage of wind- and water-power.

The combustion of wood and coal, the domestic uses of steam and hydrocarbons, and finally electricity led to the industrial age. Today in the U.S. the consumption of energy per person is the equivalent of eight tons of coal per year, compared with four in 1926, while Europe uses only a third as much—two and a half tons—and the underdeveloped regions of Africa and Asia less than a hundredweight. This difference serves to indicate the frightful poverty in which two-thirds of humanity lives, compared with the other third. Available power would have to be raised six times over if the standard of living all over the world were to be brought in line with that of America. It is a task that would be impossible without the growth of atomic power. Thus nuclear energy may prove the answer to the most pressing problem of contemporary society—the disparity between rich and poor nations.

An increase in energy makes possible an increase in man's power over his surroundings, and also the production of new materials.

The Pont du Gard has stood for centuries, although there is no mortar between its stones. Modern builders prefer solid blocks: concrete, simple or reinforced by a skeleton of steel rods, or, more recently, pre-stressed. It is the same with steel. But mining and treating the metals, quarrying to make cement and then concrete also demands energy. It is needed for transporting heavy loads, as well as for the actual preparation of materials that grow more complex every day. In both these ways it conditions the increasingly complicated tasks of the engineer and the architect.

Vast changes are on the way. People are already studying the methods of the future. Underground nuclear explosions—deep enough to be harmless—can be used to make dams, canals, harbours and inland seas, and therefore modify soil and climatic conditions, to exploit oil-fields, to liquefy and isolate hydrocarbons, thus making it possible to pump out the shale and obviate the necessity for mining fifty times the weight of ore.

Though it is little more than half a century since man learnt to fly, he is now attempting the invasion of outer space. The airman is giving way to the astronaut. Tomorrow new worlds will be explored and perhaps exploited, as frogmen hunt for treasure in an element not their own.

This is the way revolutions in the techniques of great works are coming about, more far-reaching in their effects perhaps than the methods of today and yesterday described in this book. We have two advantages over those who went before us: we know the extent of our own ignorance, but we also know that our children will discover more and more momentous secrets of the universe.

All these discoveries can help man, or they can destroy him. If he continues to pursue out-of-date international quarrels, if he does not learn to control his own instincts as he has learned to control natural energy, he will perish in the most horrible of disasters.

It is to be hoped that mankind's spiritual growth will keep pace with his progress in scientific discovery. With the realisation that in a nuclear war there can be no question of victory or defeat, but only of death, must come a solution to the crucial problem of disarmament. Only then can material and intellectual resources be freed to speed up man's tireless pursuit of peaceful goals.

JULES MOCH

Giza
and Babel

 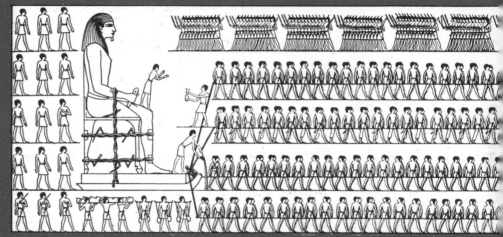

the sun
rises
on the east

One man's unaided efforts achieve little:
the united force of a hundred thousand men raises the first great monuments.

The first chapter in the history of mankind's great works opens in the teeming theatre of the East, and in the East the story remains for the better part of the first four thousand years. This period alone covers twice as much time as the seven chapters which make up the rest of this incredible story of achievement.

How could these lands of Egypt and Mesopotamia, so poor in the natural resources of wood and iron, have managed to foster so many palaces, fortresses and cities? Nature had supplied stone but human ingenuity developed brick. The root *car*, stone, is with the root of the word *mother* the most universal of all. From it come the Roman *calculus* and the French *caillou*, pebble, the English *chalk* and *cairn* and many other terms in as many languages such as the Arabic *qala* and the Turkish *kalé*.

If in Mesopotamia man developed the use of brick, it was in Egypt that he realised the possibilities of stone. This he achieved through endurance, patience and cunning. Better still was the endurance, patience and cunning of many men working together. The sculptors who carved the stern features of the great Rameses II on this cliff face had none of today's
1 scaffolding to help them*. They hewed out these effigies with their striking likenesses, from the top downwards, suspended by ropes from the cliff. Nothing could stop them, not even the pitiless sun reflected off the Nile nor their puny tools.

But the stone was not always there waiting for man to work on it. Normally it had to be hauled to the site over immense distances. One man alone was weak and powerless, but ten or a hundred men together, driven on by faith or the lash, could drag a monolith weighing several tons, and their strength could endure down the centuries. The first lesson these great works taught was the lesson of co-operation. Nothing, though, was ever built swiftly that was also solid and enduring until man had mastered how to draw plans to scale, count, measure and make a right-angle triangle. Many thousands of years of unseen, persevering efforts resulted, one day, in an unknown man taking a square and placing it against
2 a wall*. In so doing he was the true father of all the great construction works of mankind. Once this first step had been taken man could go on to create ever-new marvels.

1 Egypt. The great temple at Abu Simbel, showing the colossus of Rameses II during restoration.

2 The tomb of Rekhmire. Detail of a fresco, showing a surveyor checking the angle of a wall.

Civilisations pass, but they leave behind them giants in stone to commemorate their legends and their gods.

3 Pacific Ocean. A stone figure from Easter Is.

We shall see the treasures of the East, but first we must recognise that strength and intelligence are universal attributes, easily exportable. Today, someone like Le Corbusier can travel from continent to continent with a whole staff of architects, engineers and technicians, to erect new capitals, garden cities or monasteries. Far back in the dawn of history man may have done as much. These giant, enigmatic figures *—whose erection, purpose and date are mysteries—have been found both in the Andes chain and in the crater of Rano Raraku, on Easter Island in the middle of the Pacific Ocean, and it may be that the winds and currents of the Pacific hold the answer to the mystery.

These great, silent faces do tell us one thing: that man has always known fear. Ever since men began to band together to accomplish what was beyond the strength of one alone, they have felt a sense of mystery. Unhappy the man who tries to put himself on a level with divinity and dares to imitate the work of the Supreme Maker, the Architect of the universe! More tellingly than any other, Greek mythology recounts the punishment of the Titans, the fathers of three thousand rivers, and their final downfall at the hands of Zeus. This colossus * flung down from the temple at Agrigentum by an earthquake may be taken as a symbol

of the dreadful doom of Enceladus the titan, buried under Etna.

Even the Bible, usually so encouraging to man's efforts at self-help, fulminated against those who tried to build a tower up to heaven. The myth of Babel was deeply enough buried in the European conscience for the painters of the Renaissance to see it as the archetype of the great building work, but of the great work under a curse. At the time when Breughel painted this tower *, a monster of useless grandeur, full of machines which no one is working, Philip II was rejecting a proposal to cut a canal through the isthmus of Central America. His reason: 'It is blasphemous to alter the works of God.'

For three centuries Babel was to thwart the construction of the Panama Canal. But slowly the fear of the supernatural gave way to the impulse to imitate it. As man's mind began to grasp the magic powers of nature's wonders, so he began to feel the desire to create in his turn. The tourist slogan describing the Lascaux caves as 'the Sistine Chapel of Prehistory' is not so very far from the truth. Man developed the idea of great, permanent dwellings, either as sanctuaries for the gods or as palaces for chiefs and princes, only through first using and then adapting natural caves.

4 Sicily. The Giant. A figure from the architrave of the temple of Olympian Zeus, Agrigentum. The statue, 25 ft. high, was flung down by an earthquake.

5 The Tower of Babel, by Pieter Breughel (detail). XVIth C. ➤

The earliest sanctuaries to the gods are
carved out of the rocks by nature hersel

7 Germany. Externsteine, Teutoberg Forest. Christians added the stations of the cross to the walls of this pagan sanctuary.

The *vestibule* of the cave of Mas d'Azil
6 in the Pyrenees* forms an arch 260 feet high by 160 wide at the opening, and already points forward to interiors of vast size such as the *pronaos* of the Greek temples and the nave of Gothic cathedrals.

A quirk of nature has raised up these strange, heavy shapes in the Teutoberg
7 Forest* in Germany, where the winds of Valhalla still moan. The architects of the menhirs and obelisks would make nothing on a greater scale. The site is still capable of inspiring a strange fear, a reverent awe and wonder that makes it seem hardly surprising that these massive pillars of rough stone should have been used as altars and symbols in the rites of pagan Germany. Nor is it surprising that the earliest statuettes of the bronze age, from

Sardinia, should have four eyes and four
8 arms*, for they were the gods who built the fabulous works given to man by nature.

Man could imitate the gods only if he listened to the instructions they had provided. There were no deities more eloquent than those of the rushing waters. The first great works were inspired by the sea gods. Their secrets were known to primitive Mediterranean peoples who knew how to build ships. The ship was the first object built by man that was greater than himself: it was a mysterious and powerful intermediary between the unknown forces of a dangerous world and simple humanity. To build a ship (or a bridge across a river) was to challenge the water gods; man had to stick to all the rules or he was lost.

8 Cagliari, Sardinia.
Four-eyed, four-armed
bronze warrior.

◄ 6 France. Entrance to the cave of Mas d'Azil (Ariège).

Man learns the art of
shipbuilding from the Creator Himself.

All things were possible to the man who built with divine inspiration. A fragment of oak from Dodona, 'the mouthpiece of Athena', was built into the stern-post of the *Argo*, the ship that carried Jason and his Argonauts on their quest for the Golden Fleece. Noah received concise instructions from God: 'Make thee an ark of gopher wood; rooms shalt thou make in the ark, and shalt pitch it within and without with pitch.' It is hardly surprising that artists in all ages have been fascinated by the details of building the
9 wonderful vessel*.

Demi-gods, who may perhaps have been only supermen, have often appeared to help mankind on its way. Races as far apart as the Japanese and the Mexicans each have their own, and in Europe we have Hercules. It was he who taught the Mediterranean peoples the principles of public hygiene when he cleaned the Augean stables by altering the course of the river Alpheus. Perhaps the story that best indicates his prowess is the one that tells how the hero was carried through a sea of stars, far above the earth, in the
10 vessel of the sun*—thousands of years before mankind launched its first satellites into outer space and reported the existence of flying saucers in its newspapers.

The magic of the gods surrounded mankind's great works in many periods. In
11 Sardinia the nurraghs*, made entirely of colossal stones piled one on top of the other without the aid of mortar, are one witness, among many other fragments scattered around the Mediterranean shores, to a mysterious dark age when builders manhandled these enormous blocks into position in a way that today

9

11

9 Noah building the ark (*Nuremberg Chronicle*, 1492).

10 Hercules in the vessel of the sun. Detail of Attic bowl. Vatican Museum.

11 Sardinia. Interior of the nurragh at Torralba.

10

The stone piles are organised
into the gridiron pattern of a city.

seems little short of miraculous. Today archaeologists call these huge walls Cyclopian, because the people of classical times, having no accurate record of the authors of these amazing piles, attributed them to legendary giants.

The first great collective undertaking we know about that has no legendary associations does not belong to the Mediterranean but to the valley of the Indus. The vast ruins of Mohenjo-Daro*—a modern name meaning 'dead city'—were only discovered in 1923. Systematic investigations revealed a well-planned city, rich in works of art, which was evidently part of highly developed civilisation. But no trace of the people who built it remains. Dozens of similar cities still lie buried over a wide area, in Sind, the Punjab and as far as the Ganges basin.

We know nothing of this civilisation which existed four thousand five hundred years ago, not so much as its laws or the names of its kings. The most we can surmise is that its gods played a smaller part in the design of the city than in most early homes of mankind, for the layout of the city is severely practical.

Mohenjo-Daro already has much in common with modern New York. The buildings were of brick, the only material that would withstand the monsoons, and laid out in a pattern of broad avenues, crossing at right angles. These avenues were so planned as to be swept by the prevailing winds which, with the vultures, were the only public cleaning service available.

Certain two-storey houses even had bathrooms, supplied from a water conduit. The corbelled arches of the sewers*, built from layers of slightly jutting stones with the top rows meeting at the apex, were a primitive design that persisted in the East for twenty centuries, until the Greeks, and, to a greater extent, the Etruscans and the Romans, developed the stone arch consolidated by a central keystone.

12

13

12 India. Hypothetical reconstruction of the city of Mohenjo-Daro, by Alan Sorrell.

13 Mohenjo-Daro. Underground conduit.

Huge monoliths, standing in orderly array,
tower over the men who raise them as an act of worship.

Somewhere between 3000 and 1500 BC the most primitive of the great works we know about were erected. At the end of the neolithic period men totally ignorant of all methods of writing raised huge lines and circles of standing stones. 14 Typical examples are Carnac*, in Brittany, where three thousand megaliths stretch for nearly three miles, and 15 Stonehenge*, on Salisbury Plain in Wiltshire, where the circle of huge *triliths* includes stones weighing fifty tons and standing twenty feet high. The outer circle of blue stones at Stonehenge, each roughly five feet high, were brought from quarries many miles away. How could these people transport such heavy loads? The wheel was not yet known to them,

and the whole operation had to be done with the help of embankments, levers and rollers. For the first time and in a number of places men united under the driving force of a great religious movement, the sun cult. This cult, like many others, has vanished, and with it its priests and engineers. All that remains are the huge stones scattered as far afield as England, Brittany, Spain, Sweden, the Crimea, Palestine, India and Korea, usually near the coast but sometimes far inland as well.

From the same period dates this double line of ditches and earthworks surrounding a hill in England; a path between two 16 gateways crosses it diametrically*. This may have been the ancestor of all the

castles, fortresses and lines of fortifications that recur throughout this book.

It is possible that the megaliths of the West may have been chiselled under the direction of men from the East. The method of shaping the stone is the same as that used by the builders of the first great sacred buildings to have survived: the pyramids. Two large eastern valleys were the cradle of all our great modern building, indeed of our civilisation: the Tigris and Euphrates in Mesopotamia and the Egyptian Nile, whose fertile soil produced an astonishing crop of great works.

Nothing remains of the temples, palaces and cities—built of wood, mud and wattle—that dotted the Nile delta

14 France. Avenues of stones at Carnac, Morbihan. 2934 menhirs stretch some 2½ miles.

15 England. Trilith at Stonehenge, Wilts.

16 England. Barbury Castle, Wiltshire. Prehistoric fort with double ditch.

between 4000 and 2500 BC, testifying to Egypt's slow progress towards greatness and unity. But with the coming of bronze everything changed; it replaced iron and copper with tools capable of cutting stone. At the same time the monarchy grew all-powerful.

17 King Zoser* could command unheard of numbers of serfs. His architect, Imhotep—the first architect whose name is known to us—was also high priest, and it was his business to provide the body, which was the dwelling of the soul, with a lasting home. This home had to be built of materials that were tough and

18 Egypt. Pyramid of Snefru, Meidum. Intermediary between the stepped pyramid at Saqqara and the pyramids of Giza.

durable, and the result was the necropolis at Saqqara. Instead of light, perishable materials, this early rectangular—as opposed to circular—edifice needed beams, bricks and stone. Thus modern architecture has as its basis elements dictated by religious belief. Imhotep started a fashion, and Saqqara was reproduced twenty times within fifty years. King Snefru had an immense *mastaba*, or 18 house of the dead, built at Meidum★ in 2720 BC. This was a seven-tiered pyramid of which three tiers still tower a hundred and thirty feet above the surrounding desert.

As the Nile had its stone pyramids, so the Euphrates had its brick *ziggurats*. The name means 'hill of heaven' or 'mountain of God'. It has been argued which building came first, whether the Egyptians or the mysterious Sumerians who appeared in Mesopotamia around 4000 BC were the first to build up to heaven in this way. Both peoples seem to have been the heirs of vanished Asian and African civilisations, and the oldest monuments known to us may be replicas of hundreds of others, older still, that have vanished without trace. Sumer and Egypt are like two arches of a bridge between history and pre-history.

17 King Zoser. Statue in Cairo Museum.

In Mesopotamia the ziggurats are built
ever higher, as though men were building stairs to heaven.

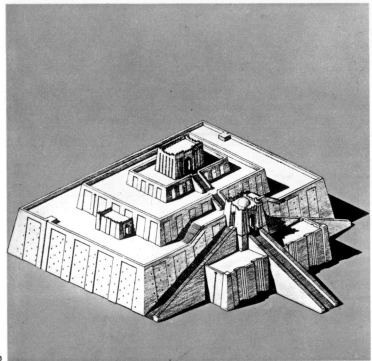

19 Iran. Ziggurat at Choga-Zambil. 20 Reconstruction of the ziggurat of Ur. 21 Choga-Zambil. The great staircase from the ziggurat, restored.

19 The ruins of one of the most impressive ziggurats of Elam, Choga-Zambil*, near the Persian Gulf, are still standing. Three of the original five storeys which rose to a height of a hundred and sixty feet, remain.

20 A reconstruction of the ziggurat of Ur of the Chaldees*, the city from which Abraham set out, shows the method of terracing which was imposed on men building without scaffolding. The bottom layer, about fifty feet high, was supported by buttresses and the mud bricks were covered by an outer layer of baked brick 21 at least two yards thick*. The upper terraces were successively smaller and lower until the topmost: this was a small temple to which the god was supposed to descend in person. The ziggurat was, in fact, a link between heaven and earth, the replica of the cosmic mountain made from primeval chaos and symbolising the original unity of earth and heaven.

Mesopotamia at this period was divided among rich, merchant cities each of which wanted to possess its own ziggurat, perhaps in memory of the mountains where the race had originated. The ideal plan of seven storeys, recommended in most of the extant texts, is seldom achieved to perfection. It appears no more than four times in the thirty or so ziggurats hitherto discovered by archaeologists: at Babylon, Choga-Zambil, Khorsabad and Birs-Nimrud. Neither was the square shape found at Babylon, where the sides of the base measured 100 by 101 yards, and again at Assur an absolute rule.

The furnishing of the temples varied widely and must have developed as time went by. In general, though, three distinct holy places can be traced: the tomb of the god, or of his substitute and his companions (this was the least important of the three), a sacred grove of cedars

Not the last building to be left uncompleted because of an excess of ambition—the Tower of Babel.

22 23

22 The Tower of Babel. Imaginary reconstruction, XVIIth C.   **23** Reconstruction by Fr. Athanasius Kircher, XVIIth C.   **24** Modern reconstruction.

24

and palm trees where the ritual union of the god and goddess took place, and finally the splendid, ornate sanctum where the gods proclaimed the fate of the land.

Sumerian teaching was that the gods founded cities with temples for their worship and men to serve in them. Hence the sacred precincts—the palace of the priest-king that was also a temple and the temple of the god that was also a palace.

Reconstructions which show as spiral the tower constructed several centuries **22** later at Babylon, immortalised as the **23** Tower of Babel***, have been proved **24** completely erroneous by modern archae-ological excavation. They are useful only insofar as they serve to bring to people's attention the differences between the pyramid and the ziggurat. The former was inhabited only by the mortal remains of princes and their possessions, the latter belonged to the living. The ziggurat was the focal point for the great seasonal festivals that were observed by all the people of these great trading towns. For this reason the pyramids have survived while the ziggurats, which were closely bound up with the fate of the cities, suffered with them the ravages of time and of human destructiveness.

25 Egypt. The pyramids of Giza. Right to left: the pyramids of Cheops (the largest, 481 ft. high); Chephren (468 ft.); and Mycerinos (206 ft.).

The Pharaohs of Egypt devote a lifetime,
and the lives of thousands of slaves, to the building of their tombs—the pyramids.

Fifty years after work was begun on the vast necropolis at Saqqara, Egypt reached the height of absolute monarchy. All local cults became subservient to one god, the sun god Ra, and all that remained was for the Pharaoh to proclaim himself the son of Ra. Cheops reigned for thirty years, just long enough to have a tomb erected for himself that would stand as a challenge to eternity. His example was followed by his immediate successors. The three pyramids of Giza, 25 shown here*, are the perfect expression of their absolute power. From right to left they are those of Cheops, Chephren and Mycerinus, and they stand in a line running from north-east to south-west in chronological order.

To build the Great Pyramid of Cheops a hundred thousand labourers were employed on the world's most immense building site. Their first task was to level the ground, and ten years were spent in merely preparing the site. In the twenty years that followed two million, three hundred thousand blocks of stone were lifted into position, rising to a height of 26 481 feet*. The blocks forming the bottom layer are over three feet high. Placed end to end, the stones of the pyramid would stretch for nearly seventeen thousand miles. The Egyptian pyramid-builders worked without cranes or scaffolding, and in all probability without even the wheel. The labourers working on the pyramid stood on huge wooden trestles, as many as there were steps, which were moved up at the same rate as the builders. The great blocks were hauled into their final positions by means of long ramps made out of brick, earth or wood and growing progressively steeper as the work went on.

The Greek traveller and historian Herodotus condemned the cruelty of such a work, costing thousands of lives. We now know that conditions of forced labour were considerably lighter in Egypt than under the Chaldean and Assyrian kings. It seems impossible that the whip alone could have achieved such results in the space of a single generation.

The great monuments still lacked their guardian. The builders of the Great Pyramid had left a knoll of rock standing near the site, and in the time of 27 Chephren* this was given a shape, that of 28 a couched lion with a human head*, possibly a representation of the sun-god, Harmachis. The Greeks called it the Sphinx, and in so doing cast a veil of mystery over this chance creation.

27 Statue of Chephren, Berlin Museum.

26 Egypt. The Great Pyramid of Cheops, Giza (detail).

28 Giza. The Sphinx. Length about 240 ft. Height 66 ft.

Knossos—the palace of Minos
gives rise to the legend of the Cretan labyrinth.

29 Crete. The palace of Minos, Knossos. Right: The great stone horns which were the emblem of the Minotaur, the sacred beast of the royal house.

Meanwhile the focus of attention has moved for a while to the Aegean. Between 1700 and 1400 BC a brilliant civilisation suddenly blossomed from a small, sea-faring people in the island of Crete and spread out to all corners of the eastern Mediterranean. The first King Minos, who gave his name to the dynasty that followed him, was the earthly represen-tative of the bull-god whose symbolic horns towered beside the first great build-ing erected to modern standards of elegance and comfort: the many-chambered laby-
29 rinth of the Palace of Knossos★.

Long before the archaeologist Sir Arthur Evans discovered it at the end of the last century, the existence of this palace had been believed to be purely legendary. Now it was shown that there

might well be at least a part of truth in the myths that had grown up about it: in the minotaur and the youths and maidens sacrificed to it, in Ariadne's thread and the labyrinth. Representations of the
30 labyrinth found on coins★ depict the ground-plan of the palace.

The fabulous Cretan architect Daedalus really existed, although his name may belong to a whole school of arts and technical developments rather than to one single person. He has been credited with many inventions, including the saw, the plumb line, glue, the cutting of the first canal, the building of a flying machine with the help of his son, Icarus, as well as with the discovery of carpentry and wood carving. Still according to legend, Daedalus studied in Egypt; whatever

30 The Labyrinth. Greek coin. Bibl. Nat.

As in Egypt, so in Greece, the tombs of royalty are conceived on a vast scale.

31 Reconstruction of interior of the treasure house of Atreus, also known as Agamemnon's tomb, at Mycene.   32 *Ibid.* Reconstruction of the entrance.

else he may have done he certainly did not invent the labyrinth. The credit for that goes back to a king of Egypt named Ammenemnes, who was the first to conceive of an endless number of passages and small rooms contained in a single palace which he built at the pleasant oasis of Faiyum.

At Knossos it was possible to house not only the king and his family, but also a numerous court in an agreeable and sensible manner which would not be rediscovered for many centuries. The building was a kind of concentric shell built around a huge central courtyard that served both to connect and light the adjacent wings. Additional rooms, private apartments, banqueting halls and domestic offices could be built on to this as they

were needed. The life of the Minoans was centred round peaceful trade, so that they could afford to build a palace entirely for living purposes; hence there are neither tombs nor fortifications.

To find noble burials of a similar period it is necessary to cross the sea to the jagged fringe of the European continent that is Greece.

At Mycene the bearded Achaeans learned from the Cretans in the three centuries between 1700 and 1400 BC and shared with them the knowledge of such amenities as the vine and the olive tree. The exact relationship between the two peoples is not clear, but Mycene may well have imported, among others, Cretan architects to carve the magnificent tombs of which the greatest has been called the

31 Treasure House of Atreus*, father of the famous Agamemnon, founder of the royal line. The inner wall is constructed in thirty-three concentric circles of dressed stone, sloping inwards and upwards to form the ancestor of all the domes in the world. It was fifty feet high and elaborately decorated.

32 The entablature over the entrance*, which is approached by way of a passage, is a stone block twenty-eight feet by four and weighing one hundred and twenty tons. This is only one of the wonders of the giant citadel with its famous Lion Gate and massive ramparts rising to a height of over thirty feet and built of stone blocks so accurately shaped that they fit together with perfect smoothness and no need for mortar.

The waters of the Nile bring prosperity to the land of Egypt, and with it, power.

33 Thebes. Prayer on the bank of the Nile.

The fellah kneeling to drink from the [33] river* mutters a prayer of gratitude while over him waves the palm tree with its refreshing shade and its profusion of dates. Generations may come and go and the gods may change, but the same [34] action links the worshipper of Mahomet* and the servant of Isis across the centuries. The life-giving waters save them both from a slow death by famine.

The first great task of Egypt is always to conserve and to make use of the waters. Thirteen hundred years separate the pyramids from the temples whose amazing origins are now to be described, longer than the gap dividing the Gothic cathedrals from the Empire State Building. The one great achievement to be attained in the interval was simply the gradual, patient taming of the Nile waters on which life depended. The people had learned to understand the annual flooding and to irrigate the valley. It is no accident that Menes, the ruler responsible for draining the plain of Memphis which connects Upper and Lower Egypt, is also known as the first lawgiver and the founder of civilised life. The need to organise vast agricultural operations at a fixed, immovable time produced a solid, powerful, centralised state. Here work had an overriding influence on political development, and political development marched hand in hand with the work of the land. There were the alluvial plains to be levelled, marshes to be drained, patches of reclaimed land to be put under cultivation, dikes to be built and irrigation canals to be dug and kept clear. When this had

been done, the land was ready for the [35] plough*.

Somewhere in the region of 1400 BC the dynasties of the New Kingdom had grown strong enough through their patiently acquired and hoarded wealth to re-establish their domination over the whole country of Upper and Lower Egypt. Some of these kings were as ambitious as Cheops and aspired to make the new capital, Thebes, into a kind of paradise of magnificent works. Two [36] colossal guardians* still sit enthroned there, to this day, to greet the visitor. Approaching the necropolis of the Valley of the Kings, one can see these stone figures from afar as they sit in splendid isolation above the fields, taller than a six-storey building and with all the appearance of having sprung by magic from the Nile [37] itself*.

The statues represent the seated figure [38] of Amenophis III* and are each carved from a single block of sandstone weighing more than four hundred tons. They stood at the entrance of a great temple that has long since vanished. We can imagine from their size the incredible proportions of the actual temple. How they were carried to their present position from the Red mountain, six hundred miles away, remains an unexplained mystery. There was no boat large enough at that period to have brought them by water. The only possibility is that a stone causeway was built across the desert to support the weight of sledges bearing the blocks, and that thousands of labourers were harnessed to the sledges day after day until the job was done.

34 Egypt. Muslim praying on the bank of a canal.

35 Thebes. Irrigation canals. Fresco, tomb of the scribe Nakht.

36 Egypt. The colossi of Memnon, Thebes. The 60 ft. high figures guard the entrance to the now vanished mortuary temple of Amenophis III.

37 Thebes. The annual flooding of the Nile covering the fields at the feet of the statues.

38 The north colossus, restored by Septimus Severus.

Thebes of the hundred gates:
the richest city of the ancient world.

39 Egypt. Temple of Amon, Luxor. Left to right: the great colonnade, the court of Amenophis III, the Naos.

Egypt's centre of gravity moved three hundred miles up the Nile, marking its progress by two magnificent achievements: the pyramids of the delta and the temples and tombs of the Valley of the Kings. The latter were the result of the intense activity of the city which for two centuries was the greatest capital of the ancient world. Thebes, with its hundred gates, stretched for several miles along the left bank of the Nile, and Homer recounts that its riches were numberless as the grains of sand in the desert. All the merchandise of Arabia, the tropics and the Sahara poured into this buzzing hive of hundreds of thousands of men.

On the opposite bank rose the sacred city, the city of the priests that complemented and occasionally opposed the king's city. This was divided into two parts: Luxor on the very edge of the Nile, and Karnak further away from it.

39 The temple of Luxor* gives the impression of rising straight out of the Nile. It was begun by Amenophis III, who lived from 1408–1372 BC and became better known as the legendary Memnon. An inscription tells us he 'built the temple of Amon of fine white stone, made the doors of acacia wood and gold with bronze hinges, and in the doors had written the name of Amon in precious stones'. A hundred years later Rameses II added to the already huge building, joining it to the even more splendid Karnak by a triumphal road lined with obelisks and colossal statues.

40 41 Picture it under construction, amid the constant bustle of the growing city, the throng of priests, merchants, soldiers and chiefs from distant tribes, while the brickmaker sets his raw clay in the oven*, labourers carry the materials* to and fro and stone-masons mix their
42 mortar*. Among them were Jewish captives taken during the wars in Syria and Palestine. The Pharaohs' military supremacy kept them supplied with an un-limited number of men and animals to haul their materials, with the sole exception of horses. What we can only guess at is the methods used by the sculptors to shape the vast monoliths of Memnon and to superimpose the stones of the great
43 columns in the temple hall*, with the statue of the god at its far end, lit only by an occasional single ray of sunlight as foreseen when the building was designed. The probable answer seems to be that they surrounded the pillars with bags of sand as they were raised and used these as stepping stones to haul up each successive block. Then, once the column was in place, the surrounding sand-hill could be taken away. At the same time the houses and gardens of the temple personnel were built in a great suburb round about. These included shops, workshops and offices and all the essentials to supply the needs of a demanding god and of the men who served him. Today nothing of Luxor remains but the bare skeleton.

40 Egypt. Detail from the tomb of Rekhmire: brickmaking. 41 *Ibid.* Carrying building materials. 42 *Ibid.* Masons at work.

**Across the river, the temples of Luxor and Karnak
reflect the pride and opulence of the priests who serve them.**

43 Egypt. Temple of Luxor. Court of Amenophis III. 'Papyriform' columns, over 40 ft. high.

Deir el-Bahri forms a link between dynasties of Pharaohs stretching over more than five hundred years. As early as 2055 BC King Mentuhotep had selected this as a site of striking natural magnificence and had built his funerary temple* against the sheer cliffs over which the sun set each evening.

In 1504 BC the throne fell to the first woman in history to become an absolute sovereign, Queen Hatshepsut. She was also the first to leave behind her a reputation as a great builder. She was the embodiment of the almost total equality between the sexes which was a characteristic of Egyptian life. Her favourite, Senenmut*, was to become one of the greatest architects of all time. He was, moreover, entirely in charge of commerce and finance, and this gave him the means to build a monumental temple for his sovereign's future resting place* which, with its splendid site and the layout of its ramps, terraces and porticoes, was to prove one of the most remarkable

achievements of the ancient world. But Hatshepsut never lay there. She may have taken unto herself all the attributes of royalty, including the royal beard, but this did not help her when her nephew (and second husband), Thutmosis III, set about destroying all effigies of his aunt and her favourite in a fit of jealous fury.

Thutmosis I, who was Hatshepsut's father and the grandfather of Thutmosis III, had been a man of very modest ambitions. He may have foreseen that the gigantic monuments which were at once tomb and temple would, by their very ease of access, encourage the cupidity of future generations. He had his own burial chamber secretly dug in a steep and deserted valley considerably more remote than Deir el-Bahri.

Others were to follow this example. The result for us is the wonderful underground burials of the Valley of the Kings, revealing the many labours of carpenters, painters and goldsmiths that went to

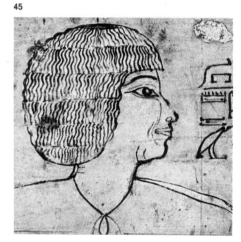

44

complete the Egyptian necropolis.

At the end of the passages and secret doorways, designed to protect the tomb from thieves and desecrators, is another world swarming with hieratic and domestic figures. Everything is shown, from the king as he was in his lifetime to gods, men and animals, and sometimes even the stars*.

44 Egypt. Deir el-Bahri, Thebes. Reconstruction of mortuary temple of Mentuhotep.

45 Egypt. Portrait of Senenmut, from his mausoleum. Thebes.

46 Egypt. View of the terraces and main temple, Deir el-Bahri, Thebes.

47 Egypt. Valley of the Kings. Tomb of Amenophis II: an inner chamber.

46 ▶

The Pharaohs are worshipped as gods; their statues dwarf the mortals who raise them.

Karnak is the last in the series of monumental works that began with Giza. The colossal statue of Rameses II, carved from
48 rose-pink granite*, seems to be extending a greeting to Cheops. When Champollion arrived at Karnak he is said to have exclaimed: 'The ancient Egyptians thought in terms of men a hundred feet high!'

Karnak is the Vatican of Thebes: thirty centuries of sacred tradition culminating in this complex tangle of buildings where the power and renown of the priestly caste shines out under the symbol of Amon, king of the gods.

The greatest kings of the golden age of Egypt all added some adornment to it, adding more and more temples, statues and pylons. Thutmosis III, who ended by far outshining the glory of his aunt

49 50

Hatshepsut, was followed by a train of kings named Amenophis and Rameses. Yet there was one who dared to challenge the
49 supremacy of Amon: Akhnaton*, the heretic king who worshipped Aton, the sun. Other kings had raised themselves to the level of gods; he was a king who reverted to manhood. At a time when the

priestly city of Karnak was shining in all its glory this weakling, an old man at nineteen, determined that his people should see him as he really was, with his pot belly and prognathous jaw. He filled the land with statues of himself tenderly caressing his wife and children, in a style directly contrary to that which had been fixed and immovable for centuries.

To get away from Thebes, with its priests and its gods, he founded the first new capital city in history, Tel el Amarna, twenty miles downstream. If Akhnaton had lived beyond twenty-five it would have extended over an area equal to that of London. But half his

dream was still unfinished when he died, and this conflict of ambitious undertakings ended with the victory of the Theban priests. The kings wisely returned to the shelter of their rule. All that remains of Tel el Amarna is a vague shape in the desert, while the great hall of the temple at Karnak still stands today, with its nine rows of a hundred and thirty-four pillars,
50 each seventy-five feet high*. It occupies an area large enough to accommodate the greatest cathedral of the western world with ease. A man who strays into this forest of stone feels himself crushed under the vast weight that defeated the 'heretic' king, Akhnaton.

◄ 48

48 Egypt. Temple of Karnak. Colossus of Rameses II.

49 Colossus of Akhnaton. Detail of a pillar of the temple of Amon at Karnak. Cairo Museum.

50 Egypt. Temple of Karnak. Great Hall of Rameses II, containing 134 columns over 75 ft. high.

Rameses II, last of the great kings, sits enthroned at Abu Simbel watching the confines of Egypt.

One of the last great works of ancient Egypt is also the furthest south. The temples of Abu Simbel are well up towards the headwaters of the Nile, some three hundred miles south of Thebes. The four immense statues of Rameses II guarding the entrance of the largest temple★ seem to look away towards the invisible frontier of black Africa, where the river has its hidden source. Yet even here the centuries of Egyptian history are telescoped, for nearby are the great quarries from which Cheops and Chephren obtained the stone they used in the delta lands. Rameses II, the last of the great pharaohs, is also the most famous because of the numerous feats of construction he achieved during his thirty-year reign. It was Rameses who filled Egypt with gigantic statues, many of which today are headless or recumbent, like this one at Memphis★. The statues were the footnote to one of mankind's greatest and most consistent architectural achievements.

It is true that in this site nature herself appears to be conspiring to abet mankind in his quest for grandeur. The king himself recognised it. 'One day when Rameses was walking in the Red Mountain he found a huge block of quartzite such as had not been seen since the time of Ra. It was taller than a granite obelisk. The god Ra had created it with his rays for a boundary.' Rameses immediately ordered it to be carved into a statue of the god Rameses. In much the same spirit the architects of Rameses II got to work on the spur of rocky cliffs dropping down to the water and carved out of them two funerary temples. The only thing that betrays the presence of their numerous chambers behind the monumental façades is the shape of the surrounding rock, recalling the pylons, or massive gateways, that were the traditional decorations of temples. (Karnak has no fewer than ten pylons.)

Entering the narrow doorway of the main temple one is struck by an innovation of which the king himself was

51

52

51 Egypt. The Great Temple of Abu Simbel, with the four seated statues of Rameses II, over 60 ft. high.

52 Memphis. Colossus of Rameses II, 43 ft.

53 Abu Simbel. Little north temple dedicated to Hathor. The statues, over 30 ft. high, represent Rameses II and his queen Nefertari.

54 *Ibid.* Queen Nefertari.

55 Thebes. Rameseum. Colossal head of Rameses II.

The Nile waters threaten
the last great work of Ancient Egypt.

proud. Although the room is carved out of solid rock in the heart of the cliff, the chamber is a perfect imitation of the courtyard of a normal temple, open to the sky. The chief events of the reign are painted on the rock like some gigantic film strip. The most famous of all ancient Egyptian battles, Qadesh, where Rameses broke the charge of the Hittite cavalry on the river Orontes, takes up forty-five feet, and there are yard upon yard of captives of all races, many of them black, giving a vivid picture of the terrific resources of forced labour needed to accomplish such an undertaking as this in a single generation.

Nearby is a second sanctuary, the Little Temple, which has colossi over
53 thirty feet high*, chambers, crypts and holy of holies, all built, like its neighbour the Great Temple, from the solid rock. Abu Simbel is the great example of architectural achievement carried out from materials found on the spot. Some of the details carved out of the cliff face, like
54 the statue of Nefertari*, Rameses' lovely queen, are well over fifteen feet tall.

For thousands of years the site had been buried by sand, and it was not until 1813 that the Swiss explorer Burckhardt discovered these wonderful temples during the course of his travels. Belzoni led an expedition in 1817 which spent twenty-two days in excavations without being able to remove more than a part of the sand, and it was not until 1910 that the temples were finally cleared. Today titanic work must again be undertaken at the site as the construction of the Aswan dam has made it necessary to protect the
53 temples from the rising water. One plan
55 is to raise the entire cliff with powerful cranes; the alternative would be to build great earthworks.

The incomparable glory of Abu Simbel is the more striking because it was the last flowering of Egyptian splendour before the sudden collapse of the dynasty. Rameses II could still build his tomb, the Ramesseum, near Thebes this time, where the ruins of one of the vast statues still
55 lie today*. Its weight has been assessed at more than a thousand tons. Rameses died just in time to be spared the spectacle of the old monarchy crumbling to dust. For the next two thousand years men would do their best to efface, by virtue of robbery and desecration, what Egypt had taken two·thousand years to build.

On Mount Sion, Solomon builds
a temple to the glory of the God of the Jews.

56 Palestine. Aerial view of the temple area at Jerusalem, with the mosque of Omar.

For fifteen centuries the city standing for all that was most significant for mankind in the eyes of the Christian West was to be not Thebes nor Karnak but Jerusalem*. Aerial photography does justice to Jerusalem's most remarkable feature: its superb natural defensive position. Mount Zion, enclosed by two steep ravines and surrounded by curtain walls, was predestined to become the site of the great Temple of Jehovah, set in its vast, man-made precinct. Today the Mosque of Omar (see page 83) adds to this the imprint of Mohamedanism without disfiguring its original impressive design.

King Solomon, in 950 BC, possessed one thousand four hundred chariots and twelve thousand horses. Gold and silver became as common as pebbles in Jerusalem, and cedars as numerous as the sycamores in the plains. . . . He caused a house to be built for Jehovah and another for himself. He employed eighty thousand men to quarry the stone from the mountain, seventy thousand to transport it, and three thousand six hundred overseers.

Then he asked Hiram, King of Tyre, for 'a man skilled in working in gold, silver and bronze and iron and with colours of crimson and scarlet and purple, and skilled in the art of engraving, to work with the artisans I have in Judah and in Jerusalem. And command thy servants to hew me cedar trees out of Lebanon for I know they have great skill. Let them send me a great quantity of wood, for the house I wish to build shall be of great size. I will give thy servants twenty thousand measures of wheat and twenty thousand measures of oil.'

This text makes it clear that the temple originated from a commercial treaty between Solomon and the merchant-king of Tyre. At this period there was a whole school of itinerant Phoenician architects, who had learned the secrets of their trade in Egypt, at work in the Middle East, ready to place their talents at the service of anyone who would pay them well enough.

They brought with them such materials (especially precious woods) and skilled

56

32

Built and destroyed repeatedly, the temple of
Jerusalem reflects the triumphs and tribulations of the Jewish people.

57 Palestine. Solomon's Temple, Jerusalem. Reconstruction by Esdras, after Chipiez.

58 Palestine. The wailing wall, Jerusalem.

labour as were lacking on the spot, and between the era of Thebes and the one at Rome they raised innumerable temples, almost all of them modelled on the one at Jerusalem. This was of the Egyptian pattern, with peristyles, obelisks, pillared halls and a holy of holies where the divine presence was enshrined in total darkness. These architects taught the Hebrew masons to cut the stones to such precision that all that remained to be done on the actual site was to assemble them. 'There was neither hammer, nor axe nor any tool of iron heard in the house while it was in building,' says the Book of Kings. Moreover the surveyors' marks which made this accuracy in constructing the stone ramparts of the Holy City possible bear a striking resemblance to those on the pyramid of Cheops at Giza.

But among the buildings of its type, 57 the temple of Jerusalem* is unique in the fame it acquired in the course of its long and chaotic history. In 587 BC it was burned to the ground by Nebuchadnezzar. When Cyrus ascended the throne of Babylon he issued an edict authorising the Jews to return home and ordered his own treasury to stand the cost of rebuilding the temple. This work was not completed until 516 or 515 BC, and bore no comparison with the magnificence of Solomon's temple. A further delay intervened before, in 443, Nehemiah, a high official at the court of the Persian king, gained his master's permission to go to Jerusalem and rebuild the walls. Little more than a hundred years later, in 323, the temple was devastated again, by Ptolemy. Judas Machabeus restored it in 164. After further destruction by the Romans, Herod attempted to curry favour with the Jews by completing the restoration of the vast terrace, though work on it was not finished until AD 64, only six years before Titus pitilessly stamped out the final revolt in Israel.

From that day nothing of Herod's precincts was left standing but the high 58 wall, known as 'the wailing wall'*. For century after century this wall has echoed the lamentations of the chosen people, and the stones have become worn by the kisses of the faithful.

Nineveh, the greatest city of Mesopotamia, until her fame is eclipsed by the rise of Babylon.

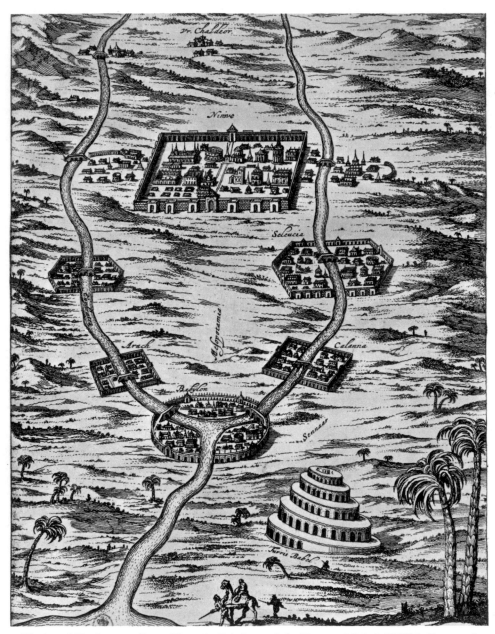

59 Tigris and Euphrates valleys: Nineveh, Babylon and the Tower of Babel. XVIIth C. engraving.

60 Nineveh. Chained gangs of slaves hauling a monolith.

the Egyptian slaves seems mild compared with that of the prisoners of Nineveh whose toil beautified the capital with gardens and palaces and contributed to the development of the continent of Asia.

From AD 612 onwards the Medes and Persians overran the land. Modern archaeology has been able to discover no more trace of the superhuman, yet inhuman, power of Nineveh than a few mounds in the desert. Now it was the turn of Babylon, a city founded much earlier at the confluence of the two rivers, to rule over Mesopotamia before she too declined.

Hammurabi had laid the foundations of Babylonian power nineteen centuries

59 This elementary map by a Seventeenth-Century engraver* bears enough relation to reality to give an idea of the essential difference between Mesopotamian civilisation and that of the Nile. The inspiration for its great works is to be traced at least as much to war as to religion. Its position as a chain in the link between two continents condemns the delta formed by the confluence of the two rivers, Tigris and Euphrates, to be the scene of continual incursions from one side or the other. For nearly a thousand years after Sennacherib first introduced his water conduits to the city, Nineveh, the capital of Assyria, retained its supremacy. These

conduits were of a size never before equalled; eighteen canals carried water from thirty miles away, and the entire system of graded reservoirs and aqueducts contained more than two million blocks of stone. Labour was plentiful, for the terrible Assyrian armies were continually enslaving the less fortunate cities of Mesopotamia, including Babylon itself. Numerous bas-reliefs, such as the one 60 shown here*, indicate the cruelty that lay behind the building of the great works in this part of the world at this time. Gangs of prisoners haul on ropes, dragging a colossal block of stone for the despotic Sennacherib's palace. The lot of

before Christ. The way in which the eighty-two articles of his Code were dictated to the great prince by the sun- 61 god, Shamash, is a matter of legend*. The sun-god is represented sitting on a stool shaped like a temple, his feet resting on a stepped footstool symbolising mountains. His head is crowned with quadruple pairs of horns. Besides laws of government the thoughtful god taught his royal pupil practical methods of organising labour and technical instructions for tree-felling, irrigating agricultural land and carrying water into the towns.

In 665 BC, just at the precise moment when Assyrian power was faltering and

The great walled city of Babylon
is the pride of its king, Nebuchadnezzar.

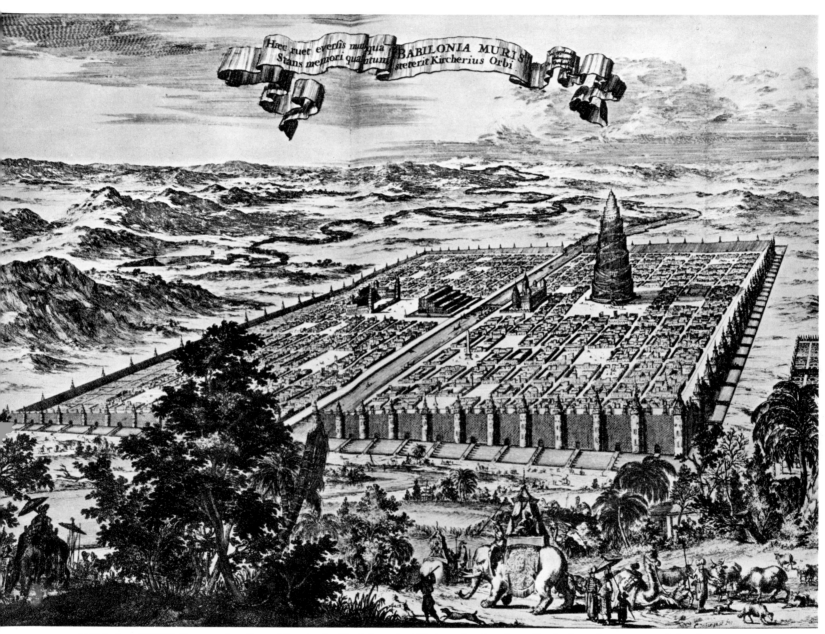

62 Babylon. XVIIth C. reconstruction of the city by Fr. Athanasius Kircher, showing the walls, the legendary tower and the river.

Nineveh about to collapse, Nebuchadnezzar II succeeded in making the second Babylon even greater than the first. Not the least of the factors contributing to the fame of Babylon has been the Jewish people's captivity there. Babylon in the Old Testament account somewhat disproportionately dwarfs all other ancient cities in pride and cruelty.

62 True, reconstructions show it to have been a city of striking splendour and unity★. Its site, on the edge of the Euphrates and two big canals, formed a rectangle roughly five miles in perimeter enclosed by two walls. The larger of these was wide enough to allow two chariots to pass on it. The eight broad gates were dedicated to guardian divinities. The Etemenanki, the Tower of Heaven and Earth, which later became known as the Tower of Babel (see page 17), rose above the hundred turrets of the outer fortifications. Each of the seven storeys of the sacred building was of a different colour. It was approached by the most splendid of all the roads of Antiquity, the processional way, paved with huge limestone flags set in asphalt. Carvings on the stones were dedicated to the praise of Nebuchadnezzar. But the greatest wonder of all in ancient Babylon was the Hanging Gardens.

61 Stele of King Hammurabi. Louvre.

The Hanging Gardens of Babylon
are one of the Seven Wonders of the Ancient World.

The Greeks included the Hanging Gardens of Babylon among the Seven Wonders of the World and attributed their creation to the great, near-legendary Queen Semiramis. They were in fact built by Nebuchadnezzar for his wife, Amytis, who missed the shady parklands of her native Media. They formed a part of the immense royal palace, and recent archaeological discoveries confirm the accuracy of the earliest reconstructions *. The series of terraces was built up to form a vast staircase planted with trees and flowers which trailed over the city walls and appeared to dazzled travellers as a perfect symbol of Babylonian power and wealth.

There was an ingenious mechanism designed to pump water from the river up to the highest level by buckets and chains concealed in hollow pillars. The water ran down gently inclined planes, supplying the plants of the various terraces on its way, and finally disappeared into underground channels which drained off the surplus. The vast construction was built on a brick foundation round a core of unbaked brick. In the upper terraces were rooms and galleries to which daylight only penetrated through a curtain of green. Within, the king and his court could enjoy a pleasant coolness which in that blazing climate had before been the privilege of the gods. Describing the building of his palace Nebuchadnezzar showed a legitimate enthusiasm: 'I completed the building of the sublime city of Babylon. My father had encircled the city by walls of asphalt and brick. I raised a third wall beside the others of asphalt and brick and joined it to my father's walls. I set their foundations on the very threshold of hell and raised their summit as high as a mountain. . . . My royal dwelling I built for a house of joy and happiness, and tribute flowed into it. I laid its foundations with brick and pitch on the ancient site, as deep as the underworld. I brought great cedars from the forests of Lebanon for the roof of it and I surrounded the palace with a great wall . . . this wall I surrounded with rushing waters as the earth by the foaming sea so that no enemy might come at it.'

From the highest terrace the king could survey the great bridge over the Euphrates, built on brick piers, the fifty-three huge temples, the two avenues, the three hundred shrines for the terrestrial gods and six hundred for the heavenly ones scattered throughout the city in a symbolic pattern laid down by its builders. Seen from this height the whole

63 Babylon. The hanging gardens overlooking the Euphrates. XVIIth C. reconstruction by Fr. Kircher.

**Of the great city nothing remains but
a wayside halt and strange carvings from one of the gates.**

64

of Babylon lay spread out like a huge flower with the sacred temple of Marduk at its centre. But, like the Thebes of Rameses II, Nebuchadnezzar's new city only attained its fulfilment as the home of a whole tradition of secular arts and crafts at the time when there was the greatest threat to its survival. A Nineteenth-Century artist's spectacular imaginary reconstruction of the destruction of the towers and temples* is a condensed version of a catastrophe which was in fact spread over a number of years, and for that reason left very little behind it.

Today there is a grubby notice-board on the railway line linking Baghdad and Basra. It reads: 'Babylon Halt. Trains stop here to pick up passengers.' Travellers seeing it may recall the curse of the prophet Jeremiah: 'Therefore the wild beasts of the desert and the wild beasts of the islands shall dwell there—and it shall be no more inhabited for ever; neither

shall it be dwelt in from generation to generation.' Who stole the colossus of Nebuchadnezzar, said to have been sculpted from five hundred tons of gold? Where is Semiramis, who, according to Herodotus, 'planted trees in the sky . . . and took history by the throat in order to publish the greatness of the kings her ancestors'?

Yet we have some direct evidence of the golden age of Babylon, standing motionless in the desert under the blazing sun and the sand-laden wind. 'Beside its gates', sang Nebuchadnezzar, 'I set huge bulls and clawed serpents, such as no king had done before me.' The fantastic creatures are still there, bearing traces of the paint that once made them even more extraordinary*. Thanks to the pitch, an ancestor of our own petroleum products, which the Babylonians used for mortar, the bricks they are built of have withstood the ravages of time and men.

64 The destruction of Babylon. Left: the seven-stepped tower. Right: the hanging gardens. After a painting by J. Martin.

65 Babylon. Dragon on the Gate of Ishtar.

65

King Darius reigns from the Indus to the gates of Greece.
He builds roads to carry ivory, cedar and gold to his capital—Susa.

66

67

In 530 BC all roads led to Susa. The Achaemenian dynasty had conquered the Medes and ruled over all the territory lying between the river Indus and Greece. An aerial view of Susa★ still shows the geometrical plan of the great Darius's new capital. It was set by its builders on a slight rise in the centre of a plain where many layers of civilisation had already been superimposed on one another, dating back to 4000 BC.

The palace, which was the focus of all the main roads in the Empire, stood on an artificial terrace, the plan of which can still be seen today. It incorporated a network of inns and royal stables, making it possible for the king's couriers to ride directly from the furthest ends of the Empire to Darius's throne room. The King of Kings★ himself, in a text that shows remarkable attention to detail as well as overweening pride, relates the manner in which this first great international undertaking was achieved: 'And the foundations were dug and the rubble packed down by the Babylonian people. The cedarwood was brought from Mount Lebanon. The Assyrian people brought it to Babylon and from Babylon the Carians and the Ionians brought it to Susa. Teak wood was brought from India; gold from Sardis and Bactria; silver and ebony from Egypt. The decorations to adorn the walls came from Ionia; the ivory from Ethiopia and the stone columns from Caria. The stone cutters were Ionian and Lydian; the goldsmiths Lydian and Egyptian and the brickmakers Babylonians. The men who adorned the walls were Medes and Egyptians. This excellent work was accomplished at Susa. May Ahuramazda protect me. . . .'

Yet Susa was not Darius's greatest work. After much thought he ordered the building of a city three hundred miles further east on a mountainous plateau where man had never built before. The human-headed bulls that guard one of its largest buildings, the palace of Xerxes★, introduce us to the world of Persepolis, 'the city of the Persians'.

66 Iran. Susa. Aerial view.
67 Iran. Detail of a relief of Darius at the entrance to the main hall of the palace, Persepolis.
68 Persepolis. The gateway of Xerxes.

68 ▶

69

70

69 Iran. General view of the ruins of Persepolis. In the foreground, the hall of the hundred columns.

70 *Ibid.* Reconstruction of the palace. In the foreground, the hall of the hundred columns.

71 *Ibid.* Persian warriors. Bas-relief from the stairway of Xerxes, the Apadana. ➤

The soldiers of the Great Kings
still stand guard on the stairways of Persepolis.

Between 518 and 460 BC the Great Kings were busy building Persepolis in the way that Louis XIV built Versailles, far away from the crowded commercial cities of the Empire. These great Persian buildings employed Egyptian and Assyrian methods to relate their monumental architecture to its natural setting. As well as massive size they began to show a feeling for beauty, in the use of space and in their harmony of proportions. The Persians brought the art of constructing terraces to a perfection that no one had equalled before them. The greatest of all these, the man-made plateau on which the capital city was built, appeared to be a natural extension of the rocky spur on which it leaned. It was strongly fortified, its defences reinforced by a double wall, nearly fifty feet high, up the hillside. Its outer face was made of limestone blocks, shaped with infinite care and put together without mortar. The only access to the terrace from the plain was by a great staircase with a double turn. Through the doorway of Xerxes, guarded by huge, winged bulls, lay the unique esplanade where each ruler built his own *apadana*, or throne room, in the spaces left by his predecessors. The effect is haphazard but not untidy, and the irregularity adds to the grandeur of the whole.

The columns here are characteristically Persian. Unlike the heavy, solid columns of Karnak they are slender and fluted, even when towering to heights of around sixty-five feet. Persepolis contained two wonders that invariably struck travellers dumb with admiration. Their remains 69 can still be seen today* and a comparison 70 with the reconstruction below* will prove a help in identifying the ruins. In the foreground is the Hall of a Hundred Columns, the scene of military assemblies. Up the great stairway, broad enough to be climbed on horseback, the Immortals, the soldiery who were the backbone of Persian power, live up to their name. Bas-reliefs of black marble show them carrying their spears, with their hair and beards meticulously curled in accordance 71 with strict regulations*.

In the background is the Apadana of Darius and Xerxes. Only a few of the columns, sixty-five feet high, which supported the vast beams of the ceiling, are still standing today, making a striking contrast with the vast plain. There was no wood on the spot, but this was no deterrent. Cedars were brought from Lebanon over chains of mountains at enormous cost. The fantastic wooden designs which came into being as an Emperor's whim vanished with the Achaemenian dynasty. But the clay designs which were already several centuries old, clever, practical and attractive and deeply rooted in the climate and ways of the land, were to become a source of inspiration for all Iran and even beyond, to Byzantium and from there to the whole realm of Islam.

71

In the cliff tombs of Naksh-i-Rustam
the Persian kings, Darius and Xerxes, rest in peace.

Less than two centuries after their foundation the great Persian cities were no more. In 330 BC Alexander conquered Persepolis, and the whole city, including the roof of the apadana was destroyed in a disastrous fire. Traces of the precious woods of which this was made have been found buried in the debris. Was the fire deliberate? Or was it, as many think nowadays, an accident whose effects were increased by the depredations of robbers during the following decades?

72 The tombs* of the Great Kings had been prudently carved by their architects high up in the sheer cliffs of Naksh-i-Rustam. This had been a sacred region from time immemorial, and here, in the so-called 'mountain of the gods', slept Darius II, the great Darius I, Xerxes and Artaxerxes. Each of the four tombs is built to the same pattern with the same façade. Only Darius took the trouble to leave any more personal traces. He had a solemn warning to posterity carved in Persian, Elamite and Babylonian, not to efface or destroy his monument. But although man respected the royal tombs the sands of the desert effectively covered the magnificent ruins of Persepolis until archaeologists cleared it away and brought the grave courtiers, magistrates and

73 priests* back to the light of day, as well

74 as these chisel marks left by the builders* at the base of a column.

72

73 74

72 Iran. Achaemenid tombs, Naksh-i-Rustam. Tomb of Xerxes, left; tomb of Darius I, right.

73 Iran. Persian dignitaries. Bas-relief from Persepolis.

74 Iran. Craftsmen's marks at the base of a Treasury column, Persepolis.

Athens
and Nara

2

order
and beauty

The Etruscans harness the pull of gravity
to perfect the brick arch, and transmit this secret to the Romans.

Alexander's conquest of Persepolis marked a great turning point. It also marked an important step in the way by which the Eastern tradition of great constructional works spread to the West. The Hittites had already served as a bridge. From 1600 to 1200 BC this nomadic people controlled the main trade routes throughout Asia Minor (modern Anatolia). They became experts in military construction, building powerfully fortified cross-road towns, often covering an enormous area. Their capital, Boghazkeny, was ringed by rectangular towers with interconnecting curtain walls a hundred feet long and thirty wide. Narrow lanes led through massive carved gates, like those of Alaja-Hüyük*, to an inner fortified square standing at the entrance to the town. One historian has written: 'Battlements, towers and gates surrounding a courtyard and a series of keeps recur in fortifications of the Ancient World; they were taken up by Byzantium and then copied in Arab castles and brought to Europe by the crusaders.'

The *hilani*, or Hittite twin towers, were at first used only to defend gates and were the true ancestor of our own keeps. The Syrians built them in front of their basilicas, so that 'our cathedrals with their twin towers remind the historian of their ancient Asian prototypes'.

There is a historical school which claims, with Herodotus, that it was the Hittites, in an attempt to escape from their aggressive neighbours, who formed the nucleus of another mysterious people, the Etruscans. Etruscan culture began to infiltrate into the still primitive western Mediterranean from the Seventh Century BC onwards. The Etruscans cut and shaped stone blocks for building, and built vaulted drainage channels to drain the marshes.

Following on this they had no difficulty in building arched bridges across ravines. The bridge of Vulci*, all except for the upper part, which was rebuilt by the Romans, is still the original work of Etruscans. Unlike the Greeks the

Etruscans were great bridge-builders, using both stone and wood, for they were excellent carpenters. The latin word *pontifex*, meaning priest, originally meant 'bridge-builder'. Their temples were made of wood adorned with expressive clay figures*, and the Etruscans were the fathers of a tradition of sculpture that was to spread rapidly through Europe.

75 Turkey. Monolithic sphinx from the monumental gate, Alaja Hüyük.

76 Italy. Etrusco-Roman bridge at Vulci.

77 Italy. Terracotta head of a woman from a temple at Veii. Vatican Museum.

Greek traders cross the Mediterranean
and establish their cities and temples on the shores of Italy.

78 Italy. Paestum. In the foreground, the basilica; behind it, the temple of Poseidon; in the background, the temple of Ceres.

Greece herself was not the home of the earliest Greek temples. Between 580 and 530 BC, a hundred years before work was begun on the Parthenon, there were already many temples in Sicily and Southern Italy. Some of the earliest attained dimensions never again equalled. The massive columns of the three temples of 78 Paestum*, near Naples, are still standing, the symbol of a giant endeavour, while the city which surrounded them has long since vanished. These are the first great works possessing both simplicity and spaciousness.

The Greek temple is the most restrained of all religious building and

consists of a ridged roof, pillared façade, antechamber and a main hall containing the statue of the god. Materials were the plentiful local stone, and the chief motive for building a pious rivalry among the Greek colonial cities. Ships from the mainland and from Ionia poured into Italy and the western Mediterranean in their thousands, carrying emigrants to build up the trading stations of Greece's New World. Marseilles was founded originally by Phocaeans. There was a jealous rivalry and competition among these cities which found an expression in the size of their temples, to which they were continually adding in length,

breadth or height, and also in number.

Paestum is the living proof that these Greek colonists knew how to preserve their sense of harmony and human proportions even in something so colossal. The town was called Poseidonia, the city of Poseidonia, and the sea god's temple was a hundred and ninety-five feet long and ninety-eight feet wide, with thirty-six columns over twenty-five feet high. Without the pediment, its façade makes a double square. It is seen here through the colonnade of another building, possibly used for civil business. Beyond the temple is a third edifice only half the size, a temple of Ceres. The

Order, harmony, endurance—Greek ideals
which find perfect expression in the architecture of their temples.

79 Sicily. Interior of an unfinished temple at Segesta (200 ft. × 85 ft.).

80 Sicily. Reconstruction of the temple of Olympian Zeus, Agrigentum.

81 Sicily. S-shaped quarry at Syracuse, known as 'the ear'. Height: 76 ft.

columns, made of limestone blocks covered with hard, white plaster, were originally decorated red, blue and gold, giving the temple a strikingly garish appearance contrasting strongly with the neutral tones to which it has weathered through the centuries.

Inside were murals, pictures, and golden lamps lighting gold and ivory covered statues. Greek Sicily might well be called the land of temples. More than forty sprang up between 575 and 430 BC, each one dedicated to its own guardian deity.

79 The temple of Segesta*, though it is now no more than a roofless shell, still

gives a strong feeling of order and strength. Acragas, the modern Agrigento, possessed no fewer than nine temples. Violent earthquakes, however, and the fury of the Carthaginians have left practically nothing of the greatest of all Greek temples, the Temple of Olympian Zeus, called the Olympeion.

80 A scholarly reconstruction* shows that it must have been four hundred feet long, with columns over fifty feet high; the flutings of the columns must have been large enough for a man to stand inside. Colossal Atlas figures supported the architrave, one of which has been carefully reconstructed on the grass where it

fell (see ill. 4). The peristyle of the temple of Selinus was broad enough to allow two thousand people to enter at once without undue crowding. At Syracuse the autocratic tyrant Dionysus collected vast numbers of slaves, subsidised priests to stir up popular feelings and lavishly rewarded the architects and artists inveigled at enormous expense from neighbouring cities. To appreciate the magnitude of the task they were undertaking one has only to plumb the depths

81 of the Syracusan stone quarries*, the rough cradle of innumerable masterpieces and where today the lone silhouette of a single man is lost.

The origins of modern European civilisation may be traced to the Athens of Pericles.

82 Greece. Reconstruction of the Acropolis by Klenze, showing colossal statue of Athena. Right: the Parthenon. Centre: the Propylaea.

Empires sometimes crumbled and suffered defeat at the hands of small nations and city-states. The Parthenon is the symbol for all of these, dominating Athens from its hill of white limestone two hundred and fifty feet high. The rebuilding of the Acropolis after the Persian invasion of 480 BC became the highest expression of the Periclean age, a period of thirty years during which Athens surpassed all other city-states in her wealth, culture, art and power. In 82 this reconstruction of the Acropolis* as it might have appeared to contemporaries of Sophocles, the small temple on the extreme left is dedicated to Athena Nike, goddess of victory. To its right is the Propylaea, designed by the architect Mnesicles, a huge pillared gateway leading from the Sacred Way to the upper

83 terrace. The Parthenon* stands on the right with a small Ionic shrine to Nike Apteros perched on the cliff edge before it. In the left centre is the oldest temple, the Erectheion, called after Erectheus, a legendary king of Athens. Dominating the Acropolis and the entire city is a gigantic, thirty-foot-high statue of Athena. The Parthenon itself was the setting for an even larger statue of Athena in ivory and gold by the sculptor Phidias.

This building of white marble from Mt. Pentelikon was the crowning achievement of Greek art. The temple was decorated with a frieze which was one of the greatest works of sculpture in the world. A team of craftsmen, working under Phidias, carved the bas-reliefs showing the Panathenaea, the solemn festival in honour of Athena celebrated

every fourth year. The procession was here preserved for posterity in a single continuous scene depicting four hundred human figures and two hundred animals.

The rebuilding of the Acropolis was not carried out without a certain amount of conflict, and there was great argument about which tasks deserved priority. In response to the urging of Themistocles the walls, fifteen feet thick, were the first to be rebuilt; even women and small children lent a hand. Then came the construction of the city's Long Walls which defended the six-mile stretch separating Athens from her port, the Piraeus. In 447 BC the men building the Propylaea were forced to give way to the work on the Parthenon, which absorbed all the best workers and obstructed the entire western slope of the Acropolis.

83 Greece. The Parthenon, Athens. The slope of the hill counteracts the horizontal plane of the building.

84 Bust of Pericles. British Museum.

The instigator and inspiration of all
84 these works was Pericles *, the ruler who
governed Athens with none of the
appearances of power. His critics accused
him of using the money contributed by
Athens' allies to 'gild and deck out the
city like a harlot, loading it with precious
stones, with statues and temples. . . .'
They might have stopped to think that
Athens owed the greater part of her
wealth to the thousands of slaves who
toiled in the living death of the silver
mines of Laurion.

But the glory of having inspired the
great works on the Acropolis belongs to
Pericles. He was often to be seen walking
about the sites accompanied by the
architect Iktinos, the contractor Calli-
crates and his friend Phidias.

North's translation of Plutarch gives an
inimitable picture of a whole city living
in and for a great enterprise: 'And this
was [Pericles'] reason, and the cause that
made him occupie the common people
with great buildings, and devises of
works of divers occupations, which could
not be finished of a long time: to the end
that the cittizens remaining at home,
might have a meane and waye to take
part of the common treasure, and en-
riche them selves, as well as those that
went to the warres, and served on the
sea. . . . But the greatest thing to be
wondred at, was their speed and dili-
gence. For where every man thought
those wishes were not likely to be
finished in many mens lives and ages, and
from man to man: they were all done and
finished, whilest one only governour continued still in credit and authoritie.'

Ordinary life claims its own great public works:
Greek architects build theatres, stadia and colonnades.

86 Athens. Colonnade of the rebuilt Stoa of Attalus. (376 ft. × 66 ft.).

85 This column of the Parthenon★ is like a symbol of the simplicity and proportion that were to become the ideal of all the great monuments of the western world. The Greek fever for building was not confined to religious architecture. The *agora*, or market place of Athens, was also destoyed by the Persians in 480 BC. Here Pericles placed the *Tholos*, the centre of the city's administrative life, the permanent home of officials, of the Senate and the Archives. The area was surrounded by great colonnades, *stoas* in Greek, and here Athenians developed the habit of strolling as they listened to the words of philosophers such as Socrates, Diogenes and Zeno. From this habit the Stoic school of philosophy took its name. The American archaeological school rebuilt the most important of these colonnades, the *stoa* 86 of Attalus★ between 1954 and 1958. Its two floors of shops and offices bounded the eastern end of the *agora*.

Even more than the priests it was the 87 lawyers, merchants and athletes★ who benefited from the great public works of the period. The stadium at Olympia is as famous as the Parthenon itself, and the 88 arena★ at Delphi could seat seven thousand spectators at a time, while an even greater number sat on the natural slopes and platforms set among the rocks and shaded by olive trees.

88

87

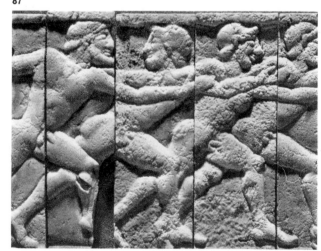

85 Athens. Corner column of the Parthenon. 85 ▶

87 Athletes. Ivory from museum at Paestum.

88 Delphi. The Stadium.

At Rhodes the Colossus, at Alexandria the Pharos: works to enhance the prestige of their builders.

Of all the Seven Wonders of the World the one that had the strongest hold on the Greek imagination, the Colossus of **89** Rhodes*, has vanished without trace. This Gobelins tapestry, illustrating the story that ships used to sail between the statue's legs, must be a highly imaginative reconstruction. All we know is that the hollow bronze statue was cast in sections and assembled afterwards, and that it was the work of the celebrated Greek architect, Chares of Lindos, in 280 BC. It represented the Sun god, Helios, the patron god of the island, and stood nearly a hundred feet high, the tallest statue in the world for the fifty-six years of its brief existence. It was destroyed in an earthquake and attempts to rebuild the Colossus by a subscription failed.

We have more information about another marvel dating from the same period as the Colossus. This was the lighthouse of Alexandria. The Pharos was the work of the architect Sostratus of Cnidos. It stood on a small island at the harbour mouth and was four storeys high, rising

to at least four hundred feet. A fire was kept blazing continually at the top where, according to visitors, there was also a mirror to reflect the light for miles across the sea, guiding ships past the reefs.

90 Alexandria*, on the Nile delta, was the first of three hundred cities named **91** by Alexander* on his travels, and has retained its importance through the ages. The city became the cradle of a new science which gained its impetus from the meeting of Greek and Egyptian knowledge. Archimedes studied there, in the shadow of the Museum and of the Great Library with its seven hundred thousand volumes. Among Archimedes' best known inventions were a water-screw, a number of ingenious defensive machines worked by a system of pulleys, and the basic principles of hydrostatics, the science of floating bodies. From Alexandria the use of applied mechanics was to spread and pave the way for a new era in the great works of mankind, whose capacities and aspirations were henceforth to produce remarkable developments.

91

90 Plan of Alexandria. XVIIth C. engraving.

91 Alexander the Great. Medallion. Bibl. Nat.

90

The Hellenic influence is carried eastward into Asia Minor where it meets the extravagant grandeur of Persian architecture.

92 Turkey. Yenihisar. Didyma: columns of the Temple of Apollo.

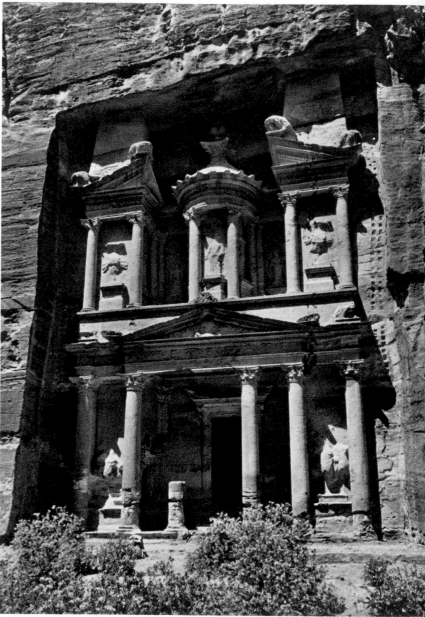

93 Jordan. Petra. The Kazne Firaoun, cut out of the cliff.

Yet another great work instigated by Alexander the Great was at Didyma, near the Turkish port of Smyrna (Izmir). This was the seat of an oracle of Apollo, for whom the people of the Greek city of Miletus built the huge temple, whose base was twice as large as that of the Parthenon. The temple took several centuries to 92 reach completion, and these two columns* from the portico give some idea of its immensity. Five rows of columns towered before the entrance and a double row encircled the entire building. The oracle, almost as famous as that of Delphi, was approached from the harbour by a sacred way four miles long, lined with lions, sphinxes, seated figures of priests, and tombs. Here we are far from the proportion and restraint of Athens and nearer in spirit to the extravagance of the pillared halls of Egypt and Persia. Not far from Didyma the powerful city of Pergamum shows a similar tendency. The monumental altar which was erected to Zeus rests on a horse-shoe base thirty feet high.

Much further east, and situated rather to the south of modern Jordan, Petra offers us one of the strangest riddles of this transitional period. Its name comes from the Greek word for a rock, and this extraordinary city was in fact carved out, with all its medley of temples, tombs and dwellings, from a natural amphitheatre of variegated sandstone. Its ruins still glitter 93 with many colours. The Khazne Firaoun* or 'Pharaoh's treasure house' (a highly fanciful appellation), with its two-storey façade, some hundred feet in height, and the curiously baroque effect of its pillars and pediments, is entirely hewn out of rose-pink rock. We have no way of telling

Bamiyan, in the Afghan mountains, is the watershed of two artistic traditions—the eastern and the western.

94 Afghanistan. Valley of Bamiyan. Cliff with gigantic statue of Buddha and caves: halls, sanctuaries and cells.

whether this strange edifice was intended for a temple or a tomb, nor what great noble built it. All we do know is that for many years passing Bedouin have let off their guns at the urn that crowns it in a vain attempt to unlock a secret door to all the treasures of the East. For a thousand years after Roman rule Petra was almost entirely forgotten by men. It has become almost impossible to reconstruct a picture of those years around 100 BC, when the city was a busy trading centre, a capital of the caravan routes between the Mediterranean and the Orient.

Much further into Asia, in the centre of Afghanistan, is a valley eight thousand feet above sea level where, at the very beginning of our era, there were monks who set up the largest Buddha in the world in the cliff of Bamiyan*. The place is a crossroads, a frontier of language, religion, art and technology, on the road which the Roman traveller Strabo called the royal way, and along which the great conquerors, Cyrus, Alexander, the Seleucid kings, the Chinese and Genghis Khan himself led their troops. The Buddhist monks carved thousands of

caves in the cliff for shrines, and sculpted two colossal statues out of the bare rock. The smaller but better preserved of the two* originally had a garment of gilded metal. Stairs cut into the rock to a level with the figures' heads gave access to chambers decorated with gold and lapis-lazuli. Galleries ran between the legs of the larger Buddha, leading to huge domed caves, also cut out of the rock, with great ribs suggesting wooden structures that must once have supported huge monuments now gone without trace.

The communities of Bamiyan have gone too, and with them the secret of their methods. These seem to have been very similar to those employed by the builders of Deir el-Bahri, and the statuary at Bamiyan has much in common with Greek and Etruscan styles in the folds of the garments and some of the faces. This meeting place of three cultures, Egyptian, Greek and Indian, situated almost at the roof of the world, is the expression in a single great work of the fleeting moment in history when contrasting civilisations which had hitherto been separate began to mingle.

95 Bamiyan. The Buddha (detail). 115 ft. high.

A begging-bowl placed on a pile
of clothes lies at the origin of the Buddhist Stupas.

97 India. Mahobodh temple, Buddh Gaya.

The first great works we find in India, after Mohenjo-Daro (see page 13) was swallowed up by the jungle, appear suddenly in the Third Century BC. Thousands of buildings seem to have sprung up simultaneously all over the Indian peninsula: buildings as varied as the dome-shaped *stupas* and the square towers which grew higher and higher with the centuries until they could justly be called the 'skyscrapers of Buddhism'.

The legend behind the *stupas* says that one day the Buddha's disciples asked him what sort of a tomb he would like. The Master placed his garments in a heap, like a stepped platform, and laid his begging bowl on top. The *stupa* at Sanchi* in central India is one of the best preserved of the oldest type; its magnificent gateways, carved to look like wood, suggest the existence of many even earlier wooden monuments which have long since disappeared.

The earliest *stupas* were simply rough mounds of earth, stones or brick, according to the materials available on the spot. There were only eight *stupas* to begin with, quite large enough to hold the ashes of the Buddha, but the religious zeal of the Emperor Asoka, who ascended the throne in 264 BC, later led to an enormous increase in their numbers.

This ruler, who claimed to be the friend of all mankind, was a Buddhist convert and did his utmost to foster the spread of the Buddhist faith, while continuing to preach religious tolerance. He was an enthusiastic innovator, and as well as surrounding himself with a female bodyguard, he built palaces and hospitals and planted trees along the roads. He was said to have divided the Buddha's remains between eighty-four thousand *stupas*. The founding of the earliest temple of Buddh Gaya* has also been attributed to Asoka. Here, under the sacred bo-tree, the Buddha attained Enlightenment. The truncated pyramid, called the Mahobodh, is still one of the principal places of pilgrimage for Buddhists. It rises to a height of a hundred and sixty feet and, despite the ceaseless adornments of later centuries, its original vaults and arches of brick and mortar have a curious affinity with the methods in use at the same period by the Sassanid Persians.

Asoka's influence reached as far as Ceylon. The Emperor surrounded the *stupa* of Ruwawel* at Anuradhapura with a veritable forest of granite columns, such as can be found at most Sinhalese monuments, intended either to mark out the sanctuary or to keep evil spirits away. As dancing was, in Hindu eyes, a form of prayer, all these early temples are adorned with dancing figures*.

98 Ceylon. Ruwawel Stupa (restored XIXth C.) and columns, Anuradhapura.

99 Anuradhapura. Two lovers.

96 India. The Great Stupa and two of the gates, Sanchi.

For fifteen centuries the
Great Wall of China fends off invaders from the west.

The Chinese, perhaps because of the need to counteract the everpresent threat from their swollen rivers, learned very early in their history how to build public works on a grand scale. From the Fifth Century BC the Hosai and the Yangtse were connected by a canal which acted as an outlet for the Great Canal which successive Emperors extended until it reached eleven hundred miles from Pekin to Hang-Chow.

But in 249 BC China laid the foundation of an even more tremendous undertaking: the Great Wall*. To begin with, thirty-four fortresses were built along a pre-determined line to serve as supply depots and headquarters while the work was in progress. All along this line armies of peasants were pressed into service to clear and cultivate the land and provide food for the workers. Convoys of provisions and materials crawled endlessly along the roads until there were so many of them that even the prowling brigands grew tired of them. Tens of thousands of labourers made bricks on the spot and hauled the vast stone blocks very much as the Egyptians had done, although they did possess the wheel and also used specially trained goats to help in the work where the ground was particularly steep. Much of the clay was brought from immense distances by long columns of coolies. Others sometimes had to travel for miles to find suitable soil before stamping it into place, or rolling it with heavy tree trunks.

These efforts resulted in a work of remarkable architectural unity: two walls about twenty-five feet high, built of brick and in places as much as six feet thick at the base. The bricks were set in place with mortar, and the workmen were forbidden on pain of death to leave a gap for so much as a nail to pass between them. The space between the two walls was filled in with clay and covered with a hefty paving of brick and stone flags, along which guards patrolled. High crenellated battlements were pierced every ten feet by loopholes calculated to give the maximum angle of vision and protection to the bowmen defending the wall. Watch-towers every hundred yards provided observation posts and living quarters for the soldiers*. The wall was built with convict labour, and legend says that four hundred thousand died in its construction. The number may be

more or less, but it is certain that all the prisons of the Empire were emptied to provide workmen because there were not enough peasants to make up the number. To these were added disgraced officials, dishonest tax collectors and many other people, including intellectuals.

Chroniclers have credited the Emperor Hwang-Ti with executing a million people, but the ruler, with 'the voice of a wolf and the heart of a tiger', may well have needed to be cruel in order to control equally violent and bloodthirsty subjects. In any case his solutions were invariably simple and basic. When he wished to impose a general disarmament he merely issued an edict saying: 'I command envoys from the eighteen provinces to bring me, by the autumn equinox, all the arrow-heads and spear-points they have, in scaled chests. Thus I may achieve peace for ten thousand generations.' Just as simply he ordered the building of the immense wall to hold off for ever the sea of Huns that periodically surged out of the inexhaustible

Siberian wastes. For the first and indeed the only time in history, in consolidating a nation, a man-made physical barrier was to have a profound effect on world development. The barbarians thrown back from the wall fell upon the West instead.

When Hwang-Ti died, in 210, the Great Wall had not nearly reached the two thousand two hundred and fifty miles that was to be its ultimate length (including nearly half of this in loops, turns and redans) through the three, widely differing regions of China: the high desert (well over six thousand feet at times), the Yellow River basin, and the mountainous region around Pekin. It was to remain an effective defence for over fifteen hundred years and therefore, by a large margin, the longest in active service of all the great works of mankind. The time of its greatest magnificence came round the year one thousand, when it incorporated forty thousand towers and two thousand fortified towns, housing three million defenders: the greatest garrison the world has ever seen.

100 China. The Great Wall.

101 One of the gates in the Great Wall, as seen by Fr. Kircher in the XVIIth C.

From the uttermost ends of the Empire all roads lead straight to Rome.

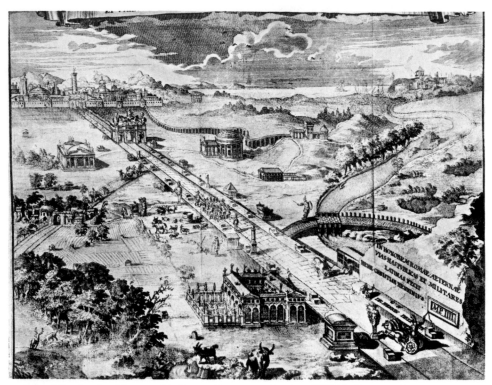

102 Italy. The Appian Way outside Rome. Reconstruction in a XVIIth C. engraving.

From the First Century BC the Romans were the undisputed rulers of the West. Their works of construction spread from Spain to the Bosphorus and from Britain to Africa. Though not themselves a particularly inventive people they made efficient use of what they inherited from others. They employed Greek engineers from Alexandria with all the latest discoveries, and they were past masters at the one art which could carry their works from one end of the known world to the other: the art of building roads.

Roman roads were first and foremost strategic. They were built to extend and control Roman conquests, so that the legions could move easily and rapidly over an ever-increasing territory, frequently taking with them ever more formidable siege-trains. The first of the great paved roads was the Appian Way, connecting Rome and Capua. It was named after its originator, Appius Claudius, and became the most beautiful 102 road in the entire Empire*.

At the height of Roman power there were twenty-nine great roads radiating out from the mother city: sixty thousand miles of main highways spanning Lombardy and Gaul as far as the Rhine, and traversing England to the Scottish border. Twice as many miles of secondary roads transformed them into a tight network round the whole Mediterranean coast and stretching inland to the pyramids and the Persian Gulf. With the exception of minor differences in the materials available the methods used were everywhere the same. The builders dug down to the firm subsoil, making a trench which was then filled with sand. On this foundation they generally put down a layer of flagstones cemented into position, followed by a layer of gravel or crushed brick beaten down hard and covered with a mixture of sand and lime one or two feet thick. This base would endure for centuries, and on top of it the 103 metalling consisted of flagstones* on which we can still trace the ruts left by ancient chariot wheels. The crown of the road was slightly raised to allow rainwater to drain away into gutters at the side. All along the road, every thousand paces, were 104 milestones*, stone pillars generally about six feet high, indicating distances, either

◄ 103 Italy. The Via Casilina on the slopes of Monte Cassino.

from Rome or from the nearest important town and bearing the name of the reigning emperor. The focal point of them all was the golden milestone that stood in the Forum, marking the centre of the Roman world. Roman roads drove straight ahead, generally ignoring natural obstacles; rivers and valleys were spanned by viaducts, sometimes two hundred yards long, hills were cleft by cuttings or pierced by tunnels. One of the greatest bridges was Trajan's across the Danube, which was nearly a mile long, but of its twenty piers not one is still standing today.

Even more than to bridge-building the Romans paid attention to building aqueducts. The Claudian aqueduct near Rome was five miles long. The shorter, but perfectly preserved, aqueduct at Segovia* which was built between 98 and 117 AD, shows the excellent materials they employed—good quality brick and stone and durable cement—and the methods of construction. The Pont du Gard*, an even greater test of Roman tenacity, consists of three tiers of arches, not as tall as those at Segovia, placed one on top of the other, making a bridge on three different levels. To avoid broken ground the builders carried their watercourse round by a long detour to cross the river Gard at this viaduct.

This is Roman architecture at the height of its power, aided, it is true, by specialist workmen available on all the sites. Gangs of slaves, under permanent foremen, moved from place to place according to the needs of building projects undertaken by various provincial governors.

104 Eleventh milestone on Via Ostiensis.

105 Spain. Roman aqueduct at Segovia.

106 France. Aerial view of the Pont du Gard.

105

106   104

59

The vast power of the Roman Empire finds concrete expression in the architecture of its capital.

107 Italy. The Roman Forum, dominated by the temple of Jupiter. Reconstruction by A. Carelli.

There was one great achievement which was to be a permanent inspiration to the rest of civilised Europe: the building of the Eternal City itself. The Romans left the business of defending the peace and security of their capital to their troops stationed far from home. Rome herself had needed no fortified walls or strongholds for many years. The city's most remarkable buildings were set proudly in a broad, marshy depression. At the junction of two main arteries lay the Forum, the great public square open to all people and to all business. The Forum was the hub of Rome, the centre of commerce, government and worship. It was built up against the Capitol* whose twin heights were dominated respectively by the

107

108 Rome: the Forum today. Top left: the Capitol. Right: the Curia.

temple of Jupiter (on the left in the picture) and the ancient, disused citadel. Between these lay the massive arcades of the Tabularium (centre), the home of the Imperial archives. Also to be seen in the picture (reading from left to right) are the Basilica Julia, given to the people by Julius Caesar, the temple of Saturn—eight columns of which are erect to this day—and, in the centre, in front of the Tabularium, the temple of Vespasian, three of whose columns are also still standing. On the right, partly hidden by the arch of Septimus Severus, is the temple of Concord, which stood in front of the speakers' rostrum.

108 A modern photograph* shows three columns of the temple of Castor and Pollux in the foreground with the Curia on the right. This edifice, rebuilt on several occasions and much restored, was the seat of the Senate where legislation was carried out 'in the name of the Senate and people of Rome'. Here too is the site of the Basilica Aemilia, destroyed by barbarian invasions and earthquakes.

The original forum was soon so over-crowded by the buildings with which wealthy Romans endowed it that the emperors surrounded it with innumerable other terraces and monuments, richer still. By doing this they gave the forum back its original character: an enormous area for people to move about in, entirely surrounded by shady arcades. Though the remains of the Roman forums are too badly damaged to give an accurate idea of these great clearings with their 109 surrounding forests of columns, Cyrene*, in North Africa leaves a vivid impression.

The building of new cities and the embellishment of old ones did in fact become two of the prime objects of Roman policy. A writer from Asia Minor, one of the remotest provinces, could claim: 'The whole world seems to be on holiday. It is flinging off its iron vesture and giving itself wholly to freedom and joy. Cities have renounced their ancient rivalries, or rather they are now moved by the same rivalry in appearing at their fairest and most lovely. Everywhere there are gymnasia, fountains, arches, temples, studios and schools.' It was a changing world. By the Second Century of our era the whole empire had become one huge building site. 'Towns came down from the steep cliff-tops where they had huddled behind the shelter of their defensive walls. They moved on to the plains where houses, squares and monu-ments could grow and spread freely. . . .' (A. Aymard).

The more or less essential ingredients of these Roman cities, new or modernised, were the capitol, senate house, basilica and rostrum. The basilica in particular, a kind of closed and covered public square with several naves, was to undergo remarkable developments. Its successive transformations were to form the basis of the Christian cathedral. But of all the great works developed by Rome, perhaps the most significant in its effect on Europe was the arena, or amphitheatre.

109 North Africa. Cyrene, showing the forum, temple, baths and theatre.

The people ask for bread and circuses,
and the largest building in Ancient Rome is the amphitheatre.

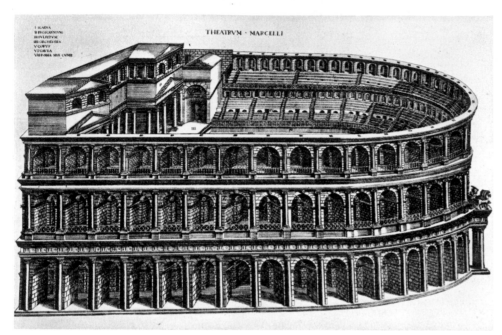

110 Rome. The theatre of Marcellus. Three tiers of thirty-two arcades. XVIIth C. reconstruction.

111 *Ibid.* Foundations of the theatre of Marcellus. XVIIth C. engraving.

For two centuries the conservative Senate nourished an inbred distrust of the theatre and decreed that all theatrical performances should be held in temporary wooden structures. It was not until the year 60 BC that Pompey built the first stone theatre in the Campus Martius. Augustus surpassed this by building the monumental theatre, not far from the Forum, which he dedicated to the memory 110 of his nephew Marcellus *. Part of this is still standing. A Seventeenth-Century engraving shows the massive size of its 111 foundations *. In Gaul people took the love of the theatre to such lengths that literally hundreds of theatres were built. Those that remain today are often very modest, but the theatre at Orange could seat forty thousand spectators. From the theatre the next stage of development was the amphitheatre.

In 53 BC a man called Scribonius Curius had the idea of putting two of the mobile wooden theatres together and staging gladiatorial combats in them. The two semicircular theatres made one complete circle, and the amphitheatre was invented.

Rome's only stone amphitheatre had been destroyed in Nero's fire. Between AD 72 and 82 Vespasian's architects 112 replaced it with the Coliseum *, which took its name from a colossus of Nero, forty-five feet high, which stood nearby. It was the most gigantic building in Rome, with seating accommodation for eighty thousand spectators on public 113 holidays. The arena at Nîmes *, which was built earlier than the Coliseum, is considerably more modest but still characteristic of the type of public buildings erected by the Romano-Gallic cities. In the Second Century a whole army of architects and workmen descended on 114 El Djem * to build an amphitheatre in keeping with the sudden prosperity of the colonial city which was then called Thysdrus. Today the greatest monument of Roman Africa, with room for sixty thousand people inside, seems to overwhelm the small Tunisian township that has grown up around it.

114 Tunisia. The arena at El Djem (ancient Thysdrus). ➤

2 Rome: the Coliseum. 580 yds. round. Arena: 283 ft. × 178 ft.   Height: 160 ft.

113 France. Amphitheatre at Nîmes. 400 yds. round. Arena: 227 ft. × 125 ft.

**The legionaries of Trajan lay out their camps
with all the amenities of the metropolis.**

115 Algeria. Timgad. Trajan's arch in the foreground; the theatre behind.

Like the kings of Egypt, the emperors of Rome are worshipped as gods; their statues attain superhuman dimensions.

The Romans, builders of roads, forums and great monuments, were above all the founders of cities. Everywhere the legions went they carried with them a ready-made, draught-board town plan. They had no need of town-planning experts for a design which sprang in the first place from religious and military demands. Thamagudi*, the modern Timgad, founded by Trajan in AD 100, is a perfect example of these numerous, geometrically planned cities, laid out on the lines of a military camp. Timgad was in fact originally a camp, made of stone and cement, three hundred yards square, set up in the foothills of the Atlas Mountains by the Third Legion. It owed its regular plan to military necessity but also in part to the direction of the *decumanus*, the principal axis of the city, which was determined in advance by the priests. The *decumanus* and the *cardo*, which intersected it at right angles, perpetuated the idea of the furrows traced by Romulus and Remus at the foundation of Rome.

The ruins of the theatre dominate the city which has been excavated from the desert, with its sewers, public lavatories, baths, and the forum, where an inscription on a gaming table brings the luxury of Rome to life again amid the sands of the desert. 'Hunting, bathing, gaming

and laughing, that is living.' The triumphal arch—attributed to Trajan—recalls sterner preoccupations, but these were at least as exciting to a Roman. The triumphal arch, which may have originated in the East as a monument to the sun, plays here the part it was specifically assigned by the Romans: that of celebrating military triumphs. Innumerable columns have been rebuilt and stand in the African desert as a reminder of another characteristic of Roman civilisation: its colonnades. At Palmyra a colonnade of three hundred and seventy-five columns, fifty-five feet tall, lined either side of the main street.

Timgad is a perfect example of the way in which the Romans set about their great building projects and the organisation of the various trades. Each body of craftsmen acted as a separate entity with its own methods, traditions and individual trademark which was carved on the completed job*, and the architects divided the work methodically among the various teams.

Work had to be standardised to a certain extent in order to produce the vast number of statues which adorned all Roman cities. From Rome the taste for statuary spread throughout the Empire. There were three thousand statues in the theatre of Scaurus alone, and in the

116 Roman trade mark. Arles Museum.

time of Theodoric it was said that there were as many statues as men in Rome. Many of these, while not equalling the colossal Egyptian statues, were still of gigantic proportions. Among them were the colossus of Heraclius* (or possibly of Valentinian), which escaped destruction as the ship carrying it was wrecked on a beach, and the statue of the Emperor Septimus Severus, whose feet* were flung down from the Castel Sant' Angelo on to the enemies of the Pope in the Middle Ages. (Although they are the only vestiges which have survived of the giant guard which Hadrian ordered to surround the top of his Mausoleum, they give a startling impression of sheer size.)

117 Italy. Bronze colossus of Roman emperor, from Barletta.

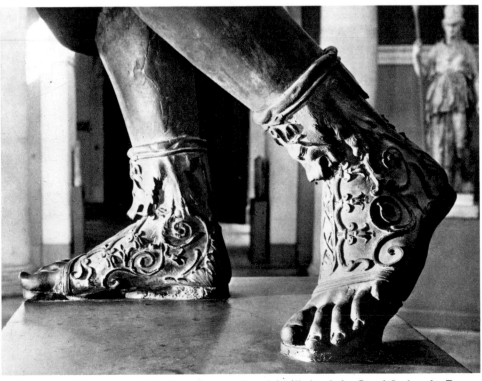

118 Fragment of the statue of Septimus Severus found in ditch of the Castel St Angelo, Rome.

Hadrian builds a villa outside Rome
for his last years, and a wall to delimit his Empire.

119

120

121

119 Bust of Hadrian, found near his mausoleum.

120 England. Hadrian's Wall at Cuddy's Crag, Northumberland. One of the best preserved sections of the wall.

121 Italy. Hadrian's Villa at Tivoli. Reconstructed model. Museum of Roman Civilisation at Rome.

All the Roman emperors, the worst as well as the best, Claudius and Nero as well as Trajan, were more or less enthusiastic builders. Their huge palaces transformed the hills of Rome, and they erected an ever-increasing number of baths and forums, besides initiating vast schemes of public works in all parts of the empire. But none of them appear to have been obsessed by the passion for building to the same degree as Hadrian★ (AD 117–138). There seemed to be no end to the ambitious projects he conceived and executed. It was Hadrian who strengthened the *limes*, the line of defence protecting North Africa from invasion from the desert, linked the Rhine and the Danube by a frontier to keep out northern invaders, and sealed off north Britain with a boundary wall★.

Hadrian also undertook the restoration of hundreds of monuments throughout the empire, in Greece and the East particularly. But his greatest work was the creation of the fantastically luxurious villa at Tivoli which bears his name. Painters and sculptors were brought from all over the empire to embellish the villa. In this reconstruction★, among the apparently disorganised crowd of buildings, a garden can be seen in the foreground, surrounded by a peristyle of white columns and with a large pool in the centre. This gives access to a huge hall, called the 'philosophers' room'. To the north is a covered walk running from east to west so that those using it could pass

As the power of Rome declines,
the emperors build no less magnificently.

easily from shade to sunlight at any hour of the day. There are also innumerable rooms, fish-ponds, galleries, libraries, to say nothing of the winter garden and the various multi-storeyed buildings about which in many cases nothing is known.

The building of such a masterpiece for its own sake, without reference to any religious, social or economic utility, was in itself a symptom of the end of an era. While the threats to the empire's borders grew more menacing, Hadrian's successor Antoninus Pius, built the temple of Jupiter Heliopolis at the ancient Egyptian city of Baalbek which had originally been dedicated to the sun-god. The six, huge 122 columns which are all that remain* give some idea of the ambitious scale of the building. They stand on a terrace of white marble slabs laid with meticulous regularity; this terrace has long been a mystery, for it existed long before the Romans came and put it to use. Its origin is lost in the mists of time and there is no reliable evidence to date it to any Egyptian dynasty, or to indicate how the slabs, some of them weighing many tons, were assembled into position. A Soviet scientist has even voiced the (apparently serious) suggestion that the builders of the terrace of Baalbek were beings from another planet who came here seven or eight thousand years ago and built an inter-planetary landing stage.

It was at the boundary of two worlds that Diocletian built his fortified palace, at Spalato (modern Split) on the Dal-123 matian coast*. In AD 305 the Roman world was coming to an end and the Byzantine world just beginning. The palace was built to the traditional plan of a military camp. One side faced the sea and had a gallery accessible to boats. The remaining three sides were surrounded by a rugged wall punctuated at regular intervals by big watch towers. Inside, the palace was laid out like a small town. Two principal streets intersected at right angles dividing it neatly into three main sections: towards the sea was the palace proper, including the temple of Jupiter (otherwise known as Diocletian's mausoleum) with its octagonal roof, and to the north two blocks of living quarters for the staff and soldiers.

122 Lebanon. Temple of Jupiter Heliopolis, Baalbek. Columns 66 ft. high.

123 Yugoslavia. Reconstruction of Diocletian's palace at Split (ancient Spalato), by Hébrard.

The seat of civil power moves eastward to Constantinople on the Bosphorus.

124 Rome. Head of a colossal statue of Constantine.

125 Plan of Constantinople. XVth C. drawing.

124 The colossal statue of Constantine★, of which only the head remains in the Capitoline Museum in Rome, was raised in honour of the founder of one of the world's most important cities. On May 11th, AD 330, the emperor initiated the changes which were to transform Byzantium into Constantinople.

125 The site of Constantinople was to become a great monument★ constantly enriched and beautified by its rulers, while three-quarters of Rome was falling into ruins. More even than Constantine, it was the Emperor (or *basileus*, as the eastern Roman emperors were called) Justinian, reigning from 482 to 565, who gave the city its particular character. At the end of his reign the visitor to Byzantium would have found eleven forums, twenty-three baths, four circuses and thirty palaces within triple rings of gigantic fortifications, of which the inner

ring was tall enough to enable its defenders to send missiles right over the other two. The domes of its five hundred churches were covered with a thick layer of gold, for the city had become the treasury of the world. The raw metal was sent from every country to be worked or turned into money. The emperor, the living incarnation of Christ in Majesty, lived in turn in a dozen palaces with brass doors. His apartments were as it were a chapel in which the slightest movement partook of a ritual. The Holy Palace, much the most important of all, was a group of seven buildings in which twenty thousand servants were employed. The palace contained concert halls, museums, beauty parlours, audience chambers, love nests, and gardens with pavilions, pergolas, fountains flowing with rose water, lily ponds.

The people too had a palace where they

could meet. This was the Hippodrome, giant circus seating fifty thousand people, which replaced the theatre and the amphitheatre relegated to the West. It was the scene of horse races of incredible ferocity, as well as of political meetings; it was the centre of public life and the place where executions were carried out. Scarcely a trace of it still exists in modern Istanbul. An oblong garden marks its 126 site★, and the obelisks which still stand there are a reminder that it was a scrap heap of all the treasure collected by the 127 later emperors. Here is the Basileus★ at the most fateful moment in the Hippodrome. He is surrounded by a crowd of eunuchs bearing sword, fan and incense, and in his hand he holds the laurel crown to be presented to the winner of the games. These games often let loose the most violent outbreaks of mob violence, so the imperial box was well protected, more

126 Turkey. *At Meydani* or Hippodrome Square with obelisks, Istanbul.

for safety than for show; high above the crowd, surrounded by walls and battlements, the sovereign was better able to face the unpredictable humours of the crowd.

It was during the reign of Justinian that two Greek architects, Anthemius of Tralles and Isidore of Miletus, erected one of the greatest and loveliest monuments of all time: Saint Sophia*. A hundred foremen, each with a hundred men working under him, raised a dome a hundred and fifteen feet in diameter and a hundred and eighty feet high. The work took five years, from 532 to 537 and collapsed twice before it was completed, possibly as a result of too much ambition. Thousands of religious monuments afterwards were to be crowned with domes in imitation of Saint Sophia. This was no longer the Roman dome, still a cautious, clumsy affair supported by a circular wall. The Byzantine dome seemed to float free and disembodied, drawing the worshippers with it to the heaven it symbolised.

Everything at Saint Sophia, it has been said, 'conspired to make space seem vast' (P. A. Michaelis). 'As the eye is drawn upwards, the space seems to grow vaster until, between the forty windows at the base of the dome, it appears quite boundless. . . . The walls of the church, with their clothing of mosaic made up of millions of tiny squares, seem to spread to infinity, to merge with the horizon, so much so that the visitor cannot fail to feel his own littleness and the greatness of the church of God.'

127 *Ibid.* Theodosius and his family at the Hippodrome.

128 *Ibid.* Basilica of Saint Sophia. Massive buttresses act as a protection against earthquake shocks.

In China, the monks of Lung Men carve gigantic effigies of Buddha in the cliffs.

129

130

At the same time as Justinian was transforming Constantinople, the Wei dynasty was undertaking vast building operations in China. At Lo-Yang, two million workers built a new capital city, to which the pass of Lung Men with its cliffs of black limestone gave access. The shrines

129 in these cliffs* were hewn by order of the Wei emperors, who were converts to Buddhism. The silk route, the route of the missionaries and builders, of new religions and sciences, brought the influence of the Hellenised kingdoms of Eurasia to the shores of the China Sea.

130 The great Buddha of Lung Men* (nearly fifty feet tall) was probably the work of a school of monks whose style was influenced to some extent by Greek sculpture.

Buddhism was not to halt its triumphant progress until it reached Japan, where, in 710, it inspired the great buildings of Nara. Nara, the first capital and the seat of the Mikado, was built on the same checker-board pattern as Chang-

129 China. Rock-hewn caves and sanctuary, Lung Men.

130 Lung Men. The great Buddha.

70

The Japanese work skilfully in wood
and build graceful many-storeyed pagodas.

131

132

133

Nan, the capital of the contemporary Emperors of China. The town itself was simply a vast park in which straight drives led past innumerable palaces, temples, pagodas and villas, all of them flimsy pavilions of all descriptions rather than buildings of solid masonry.

131 The Horyu-ji pagoda*, which dates from 730, rises gracefully from its stone base, supported by its red-painted pillars, with its five storeys of overlapping, tip-tilted roofs fanning out like the branches of a tree. Wood was to become increasingly popular in Japanese building on account of its suppleness and the way in which it

could be shaped to delicate curves without sacrificing durability. Forests of pine and cedar also made it extremely plentiful. Japanese carpenters at this period reached an almost uncanny mastery of 132 their craft*.

The resilience of wood also gave it an extra resistance to the frequent earthquake shocks which plagued Japan. The main drawback of wood was the danger of fire. The five-storey pagoda was to go up in flames five times between 730 and 1456. But the Nippons began rebuilding it at once, with the patience and swiftness of ants. It took only six years to erect the

first pagoda, under the direction of Korean craftsmen engaged by the Japanese imperial court. The first floor of this wooden kingdom was given over to a kind of diorama made of glazed earthenware, in which a hundred characters, none more than a foot high, re-enacted episodes in the life of the Buddha. To show the Master's disciples weeping at 133 his death bed*, the unknown artists who moulded this great work in clay took for their models the numerous ascetics who frequented the neighbourhood; thus we can obtain a glimpse of the people who created Nara.

In the Great Temple of the East
sits the Buddha of Nara, cast in bronze.

134

135

At Nara, the largest and loveliest wooden building in the world also houses the biggest statue ever cast*. This is the famous Great Buddha, set up by order of the Emperor Shimu in the Todai-ji temple whose name means 'the great temple of the East'. The Emperor Shimu, who was renowned for his holiness, vowed to erect a colossal statue to the Buddha in order to save his capital and empire at a time when Japan was ravaged by a terrible smallpox epidemic. To this day pilgrims come from great distances to prostrate themselves in front of the statue*. It was cast between 743 and 749 in one of the monastery-workshops where the art of casting in bronze, also recently imported from China, became such an esoteric mystery that it was impossible to draw any line between religious and secular inspiration, or to distinguish the sculptor from the monk. The metal possessed, in the eyes of the men who worked it, a character as strange and wonderful as that of jade or amber. To them alloys were a marriage of the two basic elements of the universe: the male principle, the yang, and the ying, or female principle. It was in this mystic spirit that the fifty-foot statue, whose ear alone measures nearly ten feet, was cast. The work was done in several sections which were then put together with such delicacy that the joins are invisible to the naked eye. Nearly three hundred-weight of gold had to be added to the 437 tons of bronze used in making the statue.

Thousands of miles away the monstrous size of the statue finds a counterpart in the great temple of Bhubaneswar*. It is shaped like a gently curving pyramid made up of successive layers of masonry and surmounted by a flattened, cushion-like knob. It is a typical example of the exaggerated fantasy which went into the building of these Indian monuments of around the Ninth Century; they show a mingling of Buddhist and Brahman mythology as well as borrowings from the traditions of China, Byzantium and Rome. These artificial mountains each represent an actual sacred peak. India was striving for her own tower of Babel.

134 / 135 Japan. Todai-ji temple, Nara. The great bronze Buddha.

136 India. Bhubaneswar, Orissa. The *lingaraja* temple.

136 ▶

Early Brahman legends are preserved in stone, sculpted in the cliff-face at Mahabalipuram.

138/139 Mahabalipuram. The Descent of the Ganges. Cliff 90 ft. × 43 ft. carved with men and animals.

138

139

The great works of the Brahmans in India were to stiffen Hindu resistance to the spread of Buddhism. From the Seventh Century onwards cities and palaces and temples sprang up under the sign of this conflict of influence. Such is the confusion that reigned that any precise classification is impossible, the more so as not only the same techniques but sometimes even the same teams of architects and of builders were employed by Hindus and Buddhists alike.

At Mahabalipuram, in the southern peninsula, the Pallavas decorated a whole series of caves and rocks in the Seventh Century. Scholars have long been puzzled
137 by the five pagodas known as *rathas*★. These are small temples hollowed out of the living granite and sculpted with infinite pains into the shapes of simple, rectangular huts. They are models for all the 'dravidian' architecture of central India.

Also at Mahabalipuram is the Descent

138 of the Ganges★, one of the most remarkable works of sculpture in the world, and an example of the Pallavas' mastery in carving from the natural rock. The cliff, ninety feet long and forty-three feet high, is covered with figures illustrating one of the most fundamental Brahman legends, the miraculous descent of the river Ganges onto the earth. There is a vertical rift in the rock, dividing it into two parts, and this rift has been used to make an integral part of the composition. The cliff acts as a small dam to an artificial reservoir and when the water overflows it pours down the rift, under the symbolic figure of the river-goddess, while a crowd of divinities, guardian spirits, men and animals flock together joyfully towards the life-giving waters. Only the hermit, sitting in contemplation beside a small temple with characteristic archi-
139 tecture★, brings a reminder of the deep peace and wisdom which springs also from stillness.

◄ 137 India. Mahabalipuram, Coromandel coast. Monolithic pagodas, known as *Rathas*.

75

The cliffs at Ajanta are honeycombed
with shrines, temples and cells carved by Buddhist monks.

140 India. Ajanta, Hyderabad. Cliffs and the 28 caves.

141 Ajanta. Stairs of one of the caves with sculptures.

142 Ajanta. Interior of a *chaitya*, or sanctuary cave.

Work on the temples and bas-reliefs of Mahabalipuram was still in its early stages when those of Ajanta reached completion. The steep gorge in the Deccan hills had rung for centuries to the sound of hammer and chisel as workmen cut the caves in the steep cliff face. The Buddhist monks who succeeded the earlier, unknown hermits from the Third Century transformed this ancient place of meditation into a kind of university where numerous initiates studied theology, philosophy and the arts and sciences, and which was a goal of constant pilgrimage. As their rule demanded, vast numbers of monks devoted their time and labour to building, enlarging and decorating the shrines. The result of their work was an immense network of twenty-eight cave-temples* extending far back into the cliff, many of them interconnected by narrow paths or steps*, watched over at

140

141

The three religions of India, Buddhist, Brahman and Jain, mingle in the rock-hewn temples of Ellora.

143 Ellora. The *Kailasa*. Left: sanctuary of Siva.

144 India. Elephanta, Bay of Bombay. Entrance to the cave, defaced by the Portuguese.

142 every turn by graceful, delicately-carved and strangely sympathetic figures. Between the monasteries with their square colonnades are the broad openings of the chapels, or *chaityas*, built in a style so closely connected with wood-work that the ceiling of the nave is carved to look like vaulted wooden rafters *. Inside each is a small, stylised *stupa* with a figure of the Buddha on the front. The whole of this wonderful sanctuary was created with the stone mason's simple iron and bronze tools—and, above all, with time. Ajanta is a monument to Buddhist patience, a patience that endured through centuries while the monks hollowed out a nave ninety feet long and forty high, or a monastic hall measuring sixty feet by sixty.

In contrast, at Ellora, also in the Deccan, the builders of another famous series of rock temples worked much faster and probably possessed more effective tools, provided by the kings of two energetic dynasties, the Calyoukas and the Rashtrakutas. Between the Sixth and Ninth Centuries thirty-four caves were excavated, with the aid of scaffolding, ox-carts and winches. They can be divided into three successive groups according to the three religions of India: twelve Buddhist, seventeen Brahman and five Jain.

143 The central feature of Ellora is the Kailasa temple *, one of the most astounding rock-hewn edifices ever completed. Its façade with a height of ninety feet is hewn entirely out of a single block of the cliff, and the temple stands at the foot of a vast, man-made well, a hundred and fifty feet by a hundred. The sides of this well drop vertically, and the builders must have cleared the huge central mass, foot by foot, working downwards from the cliff top and hollowing out and ornamenting the temple as they went. Around its base life-size lions and elephants appear to be supporting and guarding the temple.

144 Somewhat later, towards the end of the Eighth Century, a giant cave, indisputably Brahmanic in origin, was hollowed out on the island of Elephanta, in the Bay of Bombay, so called on account of a stone elephant discovered there. The temple has three entrances, a number of secondary shrines, and a rectangular central hall * containing a majestic, sculptured group representing Siva and his court. Elephanta marks the end of the great period of rock-cut temples. India, in the Ninth Century was devoured by a growing appetite for the colossal, fed by her numerous religions. It was time for Hindu palaces and temples to stand away from the cliff-face and come out into the daylight.

77

Indian missionaries come to the island
of Java and raise to Buddha a mountain of stone.

145 Indonesia. View of the temple of Borobudur, Java. 100 ft. high, 360 ft. broad at its base.

146 *Ibid.* Upper terrace. Buddha and openwork *dagobas.*

In the Eighth Century India's reach extended far beyond the Indian peninsula itself. Between 750 and 780, Buddhist missionaries were responsible for the erection of a vast stone wedding-cake, at 145 Borobudur, on the island of Java*, which incorporated the entire world-view of Buddhism. This artificial 'hill of the gods' contained five hundred statues of the Buddha. Fourteen hundred bas-reliefs, set in a circle covering a distance of three and a half miles, showed every incident in the Master's life, as well as the phases of his teaching. The five terraces, one on top of another, symbolised the purifying progress of the heart through wordly desires and ideals. A cunning arrangement of disappearing planes transformed the four-sided mass into an immense sphere, or upturned bowl, serving as a reminder that Borobudur was the final stage of development reached by the *stupa*. Once the pilgrim had climbed to the upper terrace he found himself in 'the place of purity'. Here, on three superimposed, circular terraces, were seventy-two small, hollow *stupas*. The statues of the Buddha in contemplation were surrounded by a protective air 146 of mystery*.

Machu
Pichu
and Granada

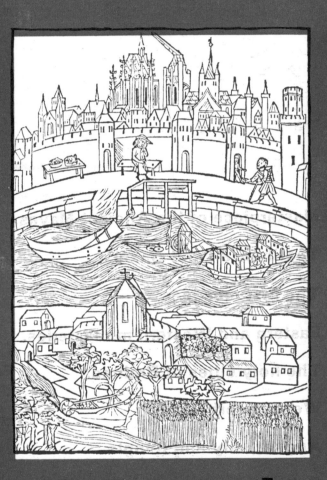

sanctuaries
and citadels

The ziggurats of the Chaldees reappear centuries later in the pyramids of Central America.

The civilisations of the American continent which we now call 'Precolumbian' were at the height of their brilliance round about the Seventh Century AD. These various races, whose existence was quite unknown to the Old World, were equally unaware of one another. Between AD 700 and 800, one of them, the Mayas, created, in what are now Guatemala and Honduras, a plethora of spectacular buildings.

147 When their architects raised the great pyramid at Palenque*, known as 'the Temple of Inscriptions', they were still in the Stone Age. They possessed neither iron, nor the wheel, yet they were able to quarry these huge blocks, dress the stone, build paved roads and manufacture lime. There was no Maya empire. Their cities were self-governing and each grew up under the inflexible rule of the priesthood. The priests were the repository of all sacred traditions and of the sciences of astronomy and mathematics, in which they were astonishingly advanced and accurately informed. These scientist-priests may have been ignorant of such tools as the saw, but they possessed more accurate observatories than any to be found in Europe a thousand years later, and they were already able to calculate the exact length of the solar year. Thousands of engineers, craftsmen, stonemasons and peasants worked together on the site of the sacred city, with its twelve pyramids and twenty temples, which grew up in the midst of virgin forest at Palenque. The people were of a slightly mongoloid 148 type*, and it may be that the Mayas originally came from Siberia. Many of the labourers were slaves, but they do not appear to have been illtreated: it was a fanatical determination which enabled them to transport huge stones on wooden rollers and shape them on the building site with flint tools and grindstones.

The immense staircase of the tomb-pyramid at Palenque spans all the terraces in a single flight up to the temple surmounting the edifice. The walls of the temple are covered with inscriptions which, if we could only read them, might give priceless information about Maya history and legend. The temple was certainly built as the tomb of a priest, though access to the tomb itself was only by way of a secret staircase hollowed out of the pyramid, whose entrance was hidden under the floor of the temple above.

147 Mexico. The great pyramid at Palenque, known as the Temple of Inscriptions.

148 Effigy of rain god, widespread in Precolumbian America.

The gods of Mexico are honoured with shrines on a gigantic scale.

149 Mexico. Teotihuacan, showing the Pyramid of the Sun (left), and steps and temple near the priests' house.

150 Teotihuacan: plumed serpent.

Little is known about the history of the strange but active people who occupied the high plateau of Mexico before the Aztecs. All we can tell for certain is that their golden age was round about the Ninth Century when the holy city of Teotihuacan* (some thirty miles from Mexico City) reached the height of its splendour and magnificence. It was laid out according to a rigid geometric pattern and, although the city grew up gradually over a period of more than a thousand years, it gives the impression of having been planned as a complete unity. Teotihuacan is a triumph of tradition and continuity, created by a society probably organised along the same priestly lines as that of the Mayas. Its oldest monument is the Pyramid of the Sun (rear of picture) which dominates the site and rises to a height of two hundred feet. The whole area of the city was three

and a half miles long and nearly two wide. The flight of steps in the foreground lead to one of the four large terraces that surrounded the sacred precinct, called 'the citadel' by the Spaniards, though it was in fact a religious sanctuary. The pyramid of the Sun, rebuilt on several occasions until it was tantamount to a series of superimposed buildings, was composed of a central core of adobe bricks faced with stone and covered with plaster. Here stone-cutting techniques seem to have reached an even greater perfection than among the Mayas, still without any evidence of iron tools. (These were to be brought to America by the Spaniards.) The origin of the pyramid is also unknown. There is a striking resemblance to the Chaldean ziggurat and also to the stepped towers of China. There are two schools of thought on the subject. One theory is that this is merely a normal

Toltec art is characterised by clear-cut geometrical designs.

151 Mexico. Wall of Temple of Mitla, Oaxaca.

coincidence: without knowledge of the arch, the Toltecs, like the Mayas, came to the logical solution of building by steps, bringing the walls of a building gradually together to form a roof. Another theory put forward is that marine currents carried the Northmen as far as Labrador or even further south and that their colonies in Europe and the Black sea coast had brought them into contact with Asiatic culture. Those who hold this theory use it to explain the grinning sculptures covering the walls of the temple of Quetzalcoatl, at Teotihuacan* and their similarity to the sculptures of India and China. Another mystery is the simultaneous use of lime for mortar in America and Asia. But opponents of the theory reply by demanding why, if there had been communication between the continents, metal tools had not also crossed the ocean. The question remains unanswered.

At all events the skill and inventiveness of the Toltec artists is there for all to see on the inner walls of the temple of Mitla at Oaxaca*. The monuments of Monte Alban which dominate this small town form a link between the traditions embodied by Teotihuacan, the Maya world and the coastal districts which may have been permeated by foreign influence. Here, for two or three generations, an important school of sculpture was at work in a somewhat stiff, mannered style, before it vanished without trace.

The same intertwined geometric motifs are to be found on the coast, at El Tajin. The 'Niche Pyramid'* is built up of six superimposed layers, surmounted by a small temple. On each level there are hollowed niches—three hundred and sixty-four in all—serving some unknown purpose. The entrance to the temple is reached by a staircase covering the whole of one side, and in front of it is the sacrificial stone, for these pyramids were the scene of human sacrifices.

152 Mexico. Pyramid at El Tajin. Gulf civilisation, Veracruz.

**Where the temple of Solomon once stood,
the mosque of Omar stands; the crescent has supplanted the cross.**

154

After the seat of power in the West had moved from Rome to Byzantium, the early followers of Mahomet set forth on a trail of conquest. Damascus fell to them in 635, Antioch in 636, Jerusalem in 638, the whole of Syria in 640, Persia and Egypt in 641. One conquest led to another. These initial stages of Islamic expansion were deeply marked by the personality of the Caliph Omar. He was responsible for bringing a degree of tolerance into the treatment of conquered lands, allowing the populations to keep their own customs and their own methods of building. The first great work of Islam, the rock dome

153 known as the Mosque of Omar*, was built in 691 on the site of the temple of Solomon in Jerusalem. It was built by Abd el-Malek, who employed architects and workmen sent especially by the Byzantine emperor. Its octagonal ground plan with a high dome surrounded by lower galleries was inspired by Syrian churches.

154 With the construction of the Kaaba mosque*, the centre for the great building feats of the Muslim world moved from Jerusalem to Mecca. Next the great Caliphs, foremost among whom was Haroun al-Raschid, turned their atten-

tion to Baghdad. Accounts of the East, dating from approximately 1050, credit the city with sixty thousand bath houses, thirty thousand gondolas and twenty-seven thousand mosques for its three million inhabitants. Unfortunately nothing has survived of the wonders of this city, and it is difficult to picture what it must have been like.

153 Palestine. The Mosque of Omar, Jerusalem.

154 Arabia. Mosque of Kaaba, Mecca. Painting on silk, from a private collection in Teheran.

153 ▶

The monasteries of the West are built according to methods learnt in the East by crusaders and pilgrims.

The first religious buildings of Islam took their place beside the great Christian monasteries built in the East by Byzantium.

In 527 the Emperor Justinian sent a whole army of soldiers and craftsmen to 155 build a monastery-fortress★ six thousand feet up the mountain where Jehovah presented Moses with the tables of the Law.

The monks spent years carving three thousand steps in the granite rocks leading to the top of Moses' mount, the scene of the episode in the Bible, and in making an approach to the mountain whither, according to tradition, angels had carried the body of St Catherine after her martyrdom at Alexandria. Despite its isolation the monastery was for long extremely rich, especially during the crusades, and its library of precious manuscripts was second only to that of the Vatican.

While the first stones of the monastery of St Catherine were being laid, a 156 basilica★ was being built at Djebel Sim'an,

156 Syria. Triple-arched façade of the Basilica of St Simeon Stylites, Djebel Sim'an.

157 *Ibid*. Remains of Simeon Stylites's pillar.

158 Russia. Bas-relief from church at Tiflis.

159 Monk harvesting (Cîteaux Ms.).

in Syria, following the tradition of the temple at Baalbek. A hermit called Simeon had pioneered a new kind of asceticism consisting in uninterrupted meditation at the top of a sixty-foot column. He remained on his perch for twenty-seven years, looking out over the spreading landscape and preaching to the pilgrims who flocked to hear him. After his death in 459, his column became the object of such religious veneration that the Emperor Zeno decided to build a holy city on the site, complete with its own monastery, baptistry and hostels for pilgrims. To prepare the terrain was in

itself a great labour. The basilica which formed the central building of the project combined three different types of church design: the octagon, the long triple nave and the cruciform. The result was four basilicas with three naves in the form of a cross, linked to a central octagon built around the famous column. Its elegant Romano-Byzantine façade was a considerable factor in inspiring the Romanesque arch which came to the West several centuries later, thanks to the numerous crusaders who came crowding to visit the famous column, of which all that now remains is the base and one

157 segment★. Originating in the East, the monastic movement had spread to the West long before the time of the crusades, and had brought in its train a wealth of great buildings.

In the West as in the East the development of the monastic centres was the same: it would begin with the gift of a 158 wealthy donor★ to embellish the tomb of some saint and result in a concentration of men all dedicated to the same religious purpose. Through the efforts of the artisan-monks the spiritual communities soon became centres of agricultural 159 development★.

The cultural heritage of the Romans
is preserved within the walls of the monasteries.

160 Greece. Monastery of St Panteleimon, Mount Athos.

161 Ireland. Fortified abbey. The Rock of Cashel, Tipperary.

162

163

162 Monks sawing marble.
163 Monks building. (Ms. Monte Cassino.)

Mount Athos is the bridge between the great monasteries of the East and the West. Monasteries, basilicas, tombs and hospices began to sprout on a peninsula of Chalcidice, in the north Aegean, between the Sixth and Ninth Centuries. The population grew to some twenty thousand, all male, for their rules would not even allow nanny-goats into the monastery. The high cliffs, falling straight to the sea on three sides, were riddled with caves in which hermits pursued their vocation of solitude and which later on held the ashes of the Blessed★.

At the other end of Europe, in Ireland, which had become in the Seventh Century one of the seats of a zealous, missionary Christianity, the monks who built Cashel★ were seeking security first and foremost. They built a wall around the area covered by their buildings, which were dominated by the church and a stairless watchtower. Here the monastery takes on the fortress-like air which it was to keep in Europe throughout the Middle Ages, but it was no longer the same vast community as at Mount Athos, able to offer its devotees a secure protection under the guardian wing of Byzantium. The break-up of the Roman Empire obliged the western monks to safeguard their essential possessions: their grain, water-supply, cattle, treasures,

library and shrine. The Huns would not wait to fall on an unprepared monastery, nor would the Normans, Saracens or local brigands.

Patiently converting to their own uses the marble they found to hand★ (this was once a Roman column), or toiling up a scaffolding with hods of freshly mixed mortar on their backs★, the masons who worked for the monks from one end of the West to the other were part of a great surge of activity that, in a smaller space, might have produced whole cities or an enterprise as colossal as that of Karnak.

The monastery of Mont Saint Michel★ took five centuries to build, and its final result is an architectural masterpiece to vie with Antiquity. To bring the granite blocks, some of them from the isles of Chausey and some from Brittany, and to raise them into position on the site was an operation made more difficult because the rock culminated in a platform so narrow that part of the buildings had to rest on buttresses against the cliff face. Romanesque and Gothic buildings, each more splendid than the last, were built on the remains of a Carolingian edifice which served as a crypt. The massive, rugged effect of the walls was relieved by the indentations, slopes and columns of the superstructure.

164 France. Abbey of Mont Saint Michel at low tide. ➤

A whole new way of life is evolved
in Europe under the mantle of St Benedict.

165 Italy. Monastery of Monte Cassino, rebuilt after the 1944 bombardment. Altitude: 1668 ft.

On the summit of Monte Cassino where the huge monastery now stands, rebuilt after its complete devastation by bombardment in 1944*, there were once two temples dedicated to Apollo and Jupiter. About the year 525 Saint Benedict climbed the mountain, threw down the idols* and decided to build a monastery there thus converting to the uses of Christianity a spot which had been the scene of pagan festivals.

The pagan idols fought back, and Benedict had to restore to life a monk whom the devil had succeeded in burying under the stones*. But still the monastery grew. By the Eleventh Century St Benedict's successors had decided to build a new monastery, capable of forming a nucleus in a rapidly disintegrating Italy. Men and women of all social degrees answered their call and came voluntarily to draw carts of stone and wood and supplies, sometimes so heavy that they required the combined efforts of hundreds of people. Some of the columns, made of a stone that could not be found locally, came by ship along the coast from Rome to the nearest port, from where they continued the journey in horse-drawn carts. Horses were soon to be used much more effectively as Europe learned from the barbarians to use them in teams for haulage purposes; the invention of the collar and the horse-shoe made it possible to use teams of horses most effectively.

The transportation resembled a pilgrimage. It often proceeded in silence, broken by halts during which the pilgrims sang hymns and confessed their sins aloud. Little by little, the monastery of Monte Cassino grew to an enormous size, but the French Abbey of Cluny, the largest in the world, was eventually to outstrip it.

166 St Benedict smashing the idols.

167 St Benedict reviving a dead monk.

168 The dream of Abbot Gunzo.

The millennium marks not the end
of the world but a renewed zeal for religious building.

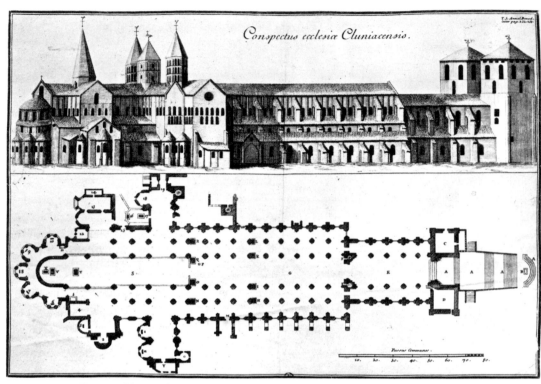

169 France. Cluny: plan of the abbey church with its five naves. Length: 200 yds.

170 *Ibid*. Model of the choir.

168 An enterprise of Cluny's scale needed high patronage. The venerable abbot Gunzo was lying ill in bed when he saw in a dream Saint Peter with Saint Paul and Saint Stephen who unrolled some cord to mark out for him the ground plan of the future church*. There is a direct connection between Monte Cassino and Cluny. The reason for Gunzo's later successor Saint Hugh's decision to attempt an undertaking which might well have daunted an emperor was his visit to Monte Cassino in 1083 which left a profound impression on him. As a result of constant effort he succeeded in laying the first stone in 1088, finding in Hezelon of Liège a builder of genius who achieved a synthesis of all the architectural advances of his time. A building was finally conceived capable of expressing the whole Christian tradition in stone, glass and painting. Alphonso VI of Castille, Henry I of England and twenty other lesser lords, a hundred bishops and the ten thousand monks belonging to the Benedictine order, which was at that time a formidable temporal and spiritual power, joined together all over Europe in 169 a drive to build Cluny*.

It was no accident that Pope Urban II came to consecrate the high altar in 1095, the same year in which at Vezelay, in company with Peter the Hermit, he preached the Crusade to free Jerusalem. When Saint Hugh died in 1109, the building was well under way and the community had already taken possession. Behind the two frontal towers a deep narthex gave onto the abbey church itself, whose size was only equalled by Saint Peter's in Rome. The nave, four hundred and twelve feet long, was flanked by side aisles and was crossed by 170 a double transept*. This unusual arrangement was necessary so that the crowd of monks could all be accommodated in the choir of the mother house. The edifice was crowned by five great belfries and towers, the tallest of which were well over 150 feet. Pilgrims marvelled at the apse with its eight columns of Italian marble ninety feet high, supporting the delicate cradle-vaulting of the roof. Architects and monks from Cluny were to cover Europe with derivations in the churches they planned and built throughout the ten great provinces of the order, from the Polish border to Alcobaça in 171 Portugal*. The triumphant way in which Cluny left its mark on the great works of a whole century makes up to a small extent for the completely pointless destruction of threequarters of the abbey in the early Nineteenth Century.

171 Portugal. Nave of the abbey of Alcobaça.

172 India. Temples at Khajuraho. Left: Kandariya Mahadeva. Right: Devi Jagadambi.

173   174

173 India. The Black Pagoda, Konarak. Sun Temple in the form of a chariot.

174 Khajuraho. Life-size statues from the Temple of Kandariya.

Sculpture and bas-reliefs cover every inch
of the Hindu temples at Khajuraho and Konarak.

In India the cathedrals of the Brahmanic trinity, Brahma, Vishnu and Siva, were being built at much the same time as those of the West. Temples were emerging from the caves and mountainsides. Some regions were in the grip of a sculptural and architectural frenzy where magnitude suddenly became the prime consideration. In one century, from 950 to 1050, the Chandella dynasty erected eighty-five temples in their capital of Khajuraho (central India), of which the largest, the Kandariya Mahadeva*, alone was decorated with 872 statues. Thanks to the quality of the sandstone, the careful use of a strong mortar and iron tenons these temples are still in a perfect state of preservation.

A later temple at Konarak, near the sea in the region of Bombay, is in danger of deterioration, but it is still the most impressive of all India. It dates from the Thirteenth Century, and its architects were over-ambitious in their attempt to make the tower of the main temple reach four hundred feet. It is still unfinished and only the *mandapa*, or accompanying building, remains, rising 230 feet over the surrounding sand. Around the bottom of the temple are bas-reliefs giving the illusion that the building is resting on twelve pairs of wheels, in imitation of the chariot of the sun*. 'The ultimate pinnacle of seven centuries' experience, Konarak marks the limits of grandeur attained by a tradition stopped short in full flight by the Mongol invasions, perhaps, but also and more simply, because it had reached the end of human potentialities' (Pierre Rambach). Close by the ruins bars of cast iron forty-five feet long and huge sculptured blocks are still waiting to be placed in position at the summit of the tower.... Here, as at Khajuraho, Hindu sculpture runs riot. Not a stone that is not carved, some into tiny figures a few inches high, others into statues standing over five feet tall*.

At the same time, in south India, the development of the *vimana*, with its tall, stepped roof, reached its apogee with the temple of Tanjore*. Here the sanctuary was simultaneously a shrine and a fortress to which the people could retreat in times of danger. But insecurity did not prevent the king Rajaraja the Great from raising the *vimana's* thirteen storeys to a height of over two hundred feet. The tower was surmounted by a dome carved from a single eighty-ton block which was raised into position by means of a six-mile ramp constructed for the purpose.

Another great work of stone subsists in the state of Mysore: the Gommatesvara of Sravana Begola. It appears that this was carved in between 974 and 984 under the directions of the monk Arishtanemi, who belonged to the Jainist cult of Vishnu derived from Brahmanism. To carve this figure depicting one of the founders of the Jain sect who had withdrawn from the world after winning a battle, the sculptors set to work on a huge block of granite found at the top of a hill, and produced a statue sixty feet high*.

175 **176**

175 India. Detail of *vimana* (square tower) of the Great Temple, Tanjore.
176 India. Colossus of Gommata (height, 60 ft.), Sravana Begola, Mysore.

The feudal barons live within the safety of round towers and massive ramparts.

177 England. Chepstow Castle, Wye Valley, Herefordshire. The Norman keep dates from late XIth C. and the rest is largely XIVth C.

In Europe a feverish activity was covering the least accessible and steepest places with towers and battlements which seemed to defy the laws of gravity. One 177 castle* among many shows how the stronghold developed between the Eleventh and Fourteenth Centuries.

To begin with it is in a commanding position, almost impossible for a besieging army to contain effectively and from which the enemy's approach could be seen while they were still far off. Its very inaccessibility complicated the structure of the castle. It was not uncommon for twenty pairs of oxen, more easily obtainable than horses, to strain for a whole day to haul a large block of stone into position. Here the rectangular keep is all that remains of 179 the earliest building—the rest of the enclosure appears to be advancing to meet the enemy. From the Twelfth Century

onwards, military architecture began adapting itself to the new methods and instruments used in war, which were themselves undergoing constant improvements. The result was the profusion of round towers pictured here, surrounded by curtain walls.

178 The architect*, the man responsible for the execution of the building, was often enough his own contractor and supervised the work in person. The bigger the undertaking, though, the more specialised the architect's job became, until there came a point when he was no longer able to supervise the overall construction and had to delegate responsibility for technical details. In the building of a tower* every man had his own specialised function, from the stone-cutters to the masons, from the mixers of mortar to the winders of winches.

178 Heinrich Yselin, architect of the castle of Berchtesgaden.

179 Building the Tower of Babel. Bedford Book of Hours. XVth C. British Museum.

179 ▶

The medieval castle is built
to afford defence but also to assert power.

181 Spain. Spiral staircase: Tower of Lonja de la Seda, Valencia.

182 Spain. The Alcazar, Segovia (restored).

183 Germany. Castle of Fleckenstein.

Here we see the banners of the princes of Naples flying in the breeze above the crenellated towers of the Castel dell' 180 Ovo⋆. Its history was a characteristic one. In the great days of Republican Rome one of the many luxurious villas of wealthy Lucullus had occupied the site. The barbarians had passed that way, followed by the Normans, Saracens, Germans and Angevins. From a resort town, Naples had become a strategic position, and the massive bastions of the Castel dell' Ovo rose directly out of the water, forming the key to the double line of ramparts guarding the town, as well as

affording protection to the harbour.

These strongholds were conditioned to withstand the impact of war, and they bore witness to the same, if not greater, architectural invention as less embattled 181 edifices. This staircase⋆ is one example, its tightly-coiled spiral making it impregnable against assault.

In spite of careless restoration the 182 Alcazar at Segovia⋆ is a reminder that many improvements to these strongholds were invented by the Arabs, in particular the machicolations added to the tops of the ramparts which enabled the defenders to pour boiling oil, pitch and stones on to

the enemy. Castles built on the steepest possible rocks discouraged attempts at undermining. But a time was approaching when even the most impregnable castle would become defenceless in face of the cannon; the castle would cease to be a bastion and acquire the characteristics of a palace. All these things were to depend on local or national circumstances. In Germany, which kept its feudal structure 183 until relatively modern times, the *burg*⋆, incessantly restored and improved, would remain for long as a challenge to the patience and resource of its attackers and as a sign of military might.

◄ 180 Italy. Castel dell'Ovo, Naples. St Martino Museum.

95

The hundred and fifty towers of San Gimignano, some of which are still standing, stark and formidable, today*, were built in the Twelfth Century, at the same time as hundreds of others like them up and down the Italian peninsula, which had become a patchwork of independent communities, all quarrelling fiercely with each other. 'Snares, ambushes, pitfalls, every form of deadly trap lay in wait in the narrow streets of San Gimignano. Guelfs and Ghibelines, clan against clan, fell upon one another, killing and being killed over the centuries. Thick chains in the main square hindered to some extent the brawls, scuffles and pitched battles between the opposing parties' (André Suarès). Each noble wanted to raise up an emblem to bear witness to his power. Often the means and the time were lacking, so that the towers raised for this purpose were square and unadorned, adequate for defence, and the materials were brought from the nearest quarry. At Rome, now become *Roma turrita*, the rapacious barons turned the great monuments of Antiquity into formidable bastions: the Coliseum, the theatre of Marcellus, the palaces, and even the arch of Septimus Severus.

In the towns, now more or less free of the feudal yoke, the building of walls to protect their merchant communities was the first concern of the burgesses*. The technicians, who had to be equally experienced in civil and military works, became men of importance with a whole code of traditions and secrets for their own use.

When the Knights Templar of Rhodes were in a desperate hurry to fortify their island against the Turks, the Grand Master of the order, reviving the old legend of the men who had built the temple of Solomon, attended himself to the reception of the carpenters*. The Fifteenth Century saw the birth of the guilds and the temporary huts which served to lodge the workmen gave their name to the Masonic lodges. The importance of manual handicrafts was highly regarded and the cult of Saint Joseph the carpenter began to spread from Rome. The rise of the artisan classes was to be

184 Italy. San Gimignano, Tuscany. Two of the thirteen medieval towers still standing.

185 Founding the city of Berne, Switzerland.

186 Grand Master of the Templars of Rhodes receiving the Carpenters' Guild.

takes the place of the knight.

attributed not only to technical progress but also to the pilgrimages, crusades and similar movements of the population which spread new discoveries from one region to the next and stimulated inventiveness. After centuries of stagnation the western world was beginning to take a few, still cautious steps forward. Sheltered behind massive ramparts like those of Ragusa*, enlightened princes or merchant corporations were gradually freeing themselves from the yoke of Byzantium, Hungary or Venice and pioneering new methods of manufacture and agriculture suited to their own conditions.

When Louis IX of France was determined on a crusade, he looked for a point on the French coast suitable for establishing a military base. Aigues-Mortes* was thirty years a-building. Alluring prospects drew thither a population of fifteen thousand souls, and although its ramparts (inspired by Muslim fortifications) gave it a military stamp, the town was principally given over to the exploitation of the salt marshes.

187 Yugoslavia. Ragusa, on the Dalmatian coast (Dubrovnik). North ramparts and Minceta tower.

188 France. Aigues-Mortes, Gard. At the north-west corner is the keep, 118 ft. high.

Today the palaces and temples of the Khmers rise in the heart of the encroaching jungle.

189 Cambodia. Angkor Wat. The main west face. Only the first floor galleries were open to the public.

The flowering of the Middle Ages in Europe coincides with the golden age of the Khmers, who had been settled in Cambodia from prehistoric times. Their beliefs differed very little from those of other Asiatic civilisations. They believed that no great community could prosper except in harmony with the universal laws. This harmony had to be expressed by endowing their capital, palace and temple with the same mythical form as that which they attributed to the universe as a whole: a series of geometric forms centred round a hill which brought the priest-king into communion with the gods.

The site of Angkor, which had been

the capital of the Khmers from 908, received its first temple of this kind about the year AD 1000. This was the Baphuon. But it was Suryavarman II (1113–1145) who raised the best preserved of the Khmer funerary temples to Vishnu. 189 Angkor Wat★ is also one of the largest religious edifices ever known. Each of the four sides of its moated perimeter is close on a mile in length. The central sanctuary combines the pyramid shape of the Baphuon with a cruciform pattern connecting the four corner towers with the central one, two hundred and fifteen feet high, by galleries decorated with bas-reliefs. Other external galleries are linked

by more towers, the whole forming a huge mass of successive terraces and galleries with a clearly visible rectangular plan. The first floor galleries were probably the only ones to which the people were allowed access. There they could read in stone the legendary stories of the sacred epics: the *Ramayana* (eighty thousand lines), and the *Mahabharata* (two hundred thousand lines).

Angkor Wat, however, was not to be the only temple at Angkor. Beside it, Jayavarman II (1118–1201) built Angkor Thom, a fortified square enclosed by a moat more than eight miles long. At the centre of this sacred fortress-city he built

The bearers of the Sacred Serpent
of the Bayon carry out their office with becoming dignity.

190 Angkor Thom. Southern causeway. Stone giants bearing the sacred serpent.

191 *Ibid.* The Bayon. Giant sculptured heads.

the temple of the Bayon, which was approached by causeways whose balustrades were carved to represent the *nagas*, sacred serpents, held in the arms of their 190 giant keepers*. The Bayon, as massive as Angkor Wat, symbolised mount Meru, the axis of the world. It was dedicated to King Buddha, the emblem of royal power, and became the centre of the realm. 'Similar to a lens, it became a concentration of all the divine powers of heaven and earth, which it reflected on to the Empire' (Ernst Diez). The gigantic human faces decorating each of the four sides of the fifty-two stone towers could equally well be Buddha or Jayavarman

191 himself*, so majestic is their expression.

One thing, though, is certain; these eight-foot high faces, turned towards the four points of the compass, were an affirmation of the religious and civil power of the Khmer monarchy over the kingdom as a whole. At the summit of his temple-hill the king became a god even in his own lifetime by virtue of the mystical union which he had each night with the nine-headed serpent who appeared to him as a woman and shared his bed.

This splendid capital was all too soon to be overwhelmed by the encroachments of the tropical jungle.

The most majestic house in the city is the House of God; to adorn it each craftsman gives of his best.

192 France. Nave of the cathedral of Coutances. Height: 90 ft.

stone had to be moved even than during the construction of the pyramids of Giza. The foundations of the great cathedrals were laid over thirty feet deep and in some cases took up as much room as the visible portion of the building.

Tradition has it that an entire town would work together, animated by a common purpose, to raise its cathedral. This is not altogether true. The whole town would have contributed its prayers as well as offerings of money or in kind, very probably; everyone might have lent a hand on occasions when a particularly large block had to be raised. But the bulk of the work remained the province of 195 trained builders* who were gaining continual experience. The floating labour force, free and relatively well paid, and comparable in many ways to the dam builders of the Twentieth Century, certainly experienced very little idleness in that period—except on the forty to forty-five ecclesiastical feast days when work was forbidden. Otherwise work went on almost without stop from sunrise to sunset, even on the longest summer days. Stone had to be cut, the roof had to

One of the most enduring legacies of the later Middle Ages was the Gothic 192 Cathedral*, whose graceful vertical lines invited men to raise their thoughts on high. It was a miracle which recurred over and over again on innumerable 193 sites*. Despite its name, the Gothic cathedral originated in France. The early experiments were at Sens in 1133, Noyon in 1151, Laon in 1160. With greater confidence, and therefore with greater ambition, the builders raised the cathedrals of Paris 1163, Bourges 1192, Chartres 1194, Rouen 1202, Reims 1211, Le Mans 1217. (The dates are those when

work on the cathedrals was begun.) The climax was reached in 1247 with Beauvais, where the choir was so superb that the rest of the building could not match it.

Meanwhile at Amiens the most har-194 monious, as well as the largest, cathedral* in France was built. It was large enough to contain the entire population of the town, which was then ten thousand people.

Thousands of tons of stone were quarried in France alone between 1050 and 1350, enough to build eighty cathedrals, hundreds of great churches and thousands of small parish churches. More

193 Building a church. Très riches heures du duc de Berry.

194 France. Aerial view of Amiens cathedral, south face. 160 yds. long by 35 yds. wide. Height of nave: 140 ft.

receive its coat of lead, and the glass for the windows had to be prepared. The stained-glass windows were originally made on the spot, but the great cathedrals came to use such a quantity of glass that it soon became necessary to obtain it from the makers whose furnaces were on the edges of the forests.

The colouring was still done on the spot, probably by artisans who set up shop wherever they happened to be in demand. Thus it was possible for them to 'judge on the spot the colours needed, according to whether the window to be glazed faced north, south, east or west,

whether it opened straight on to the sky or was sheltered by a buttress or shaded by a tower, as well as according to whether it lighted a dark or bright corner of the building, pale or coloured; and they were able to decide upon the depth of coloration of one window in relation to its neighbour' (Marcel Aubert). In thirty years the glass painters who worked at Chartres, after the old cathedral had been burned down in 1194, completed 173 windows, a surface area of 2600 square metres. Of these stained-glass windows sixteen were donated by the clergy, forty-four by princes and forty-two by the guilds.

195 Building the cathedral at Modena.

Experience, not theory, teaches the cathedral-builder his art.

196

The Gothic style spread to England, where it reached Salisbury, Peterborough and many other cities. In Spain it left its mark on such towns as Burgos, Leon and Toledo. It spread to Portugal. It was less successful in Italy, but touched places as far afield as Hungary and Palestine and flourished in Germany in particular, where twenty superb cathedrals were built. The stone tracery of the spire of 196 Münster*, soaring to over five hundred feet, shows the distance covered by ecclesiastical architecture since the 197 moment when the builder of Albi* raised his fortress-church in 1282, using bricks made from the local clay. The work was 198 becoming increasingly complex*. It was necessary to calculate the thickness of the stones, the size of apertures, the positioning of buttresses, the placing of the countless sculptures. All this involved a knowledge of considerably more than the rudiments of geometry, of statics and of the properties of the materials employed. In the absence of any formal scientific training, the master craftsmen had a store of practical experience which was handed down carefully from master to apprentice and afterwards lost. The building of the Gothic cathedrals was not without its element of mystery.

198

198 Detail from triptych of the Guild of Masons, Antwerp.

◄ 196 Germany. Spire of Münster Cathedral.

197 France. Albi. The cathedral, from the south-east. ►

High in the Peruvian Andes the monolithic remains of the Inca civilisation still stand, veiled in mystery.

200 Peru. Fort of Sacsahuaman, near Cuzco. Triple ramparts, stepped back. Some of the polygonal blocks are over 20 ft. high.

199 High up in the Andes, a few hours away from Cuzco, the ancient capital of the Incas, stands Machu Pichu*. This fortress-city, abandoned for some unexplained reason, was built by some astonishing feat in a high valley nearly seven thousand feet above sea level. Ten thousand people lived in this concentration of sun-temples, royal palaces, gardens, houses, broad stairways and narrow flights of steps. They left it to cultivate their fields which climbed steeply up the mountainside in a thousand tiny terraces, and to draw water from the giant reservoirs hollowed out of the rock. Its origins can only be guessed at. Some authorities hold that Machu Pichu was founded as far back as 4000 BC, but in 1000 AD the Incas were at the height of their Empire and covered the 'Holy Valley', of which this town may be only an outcrop, with strong dykes, canals, watch-towers and forts.

The Incas embellished the rectangular square of Machu Pichu, which, with its extensions, divided the city into two halves, by building their monuments distinguished by trapezoid doors. They cut afresh the steep path leading up to the observatory of the Sun, two thousand feet further up on the topmost summit of Huayna Pichu, from where this picture was taken. At this period they had the advantage over all the other peoples of America in their knowledge of bronze, though they did not possess either the wheel, iron or a coinage.

200 Not far from Machu Pichu, but lower down, stands the fortress of Sacsahuaman* protected by its triple-tiered ramparts of massive blocks. The outer wall extends over two miles and is made of blocks of stone, some of them measuring twenty feet by ten, laid without mortar; the irregular pattern of the wall was probably devised as a way to counteract shuddering effects of earthquake shocks.

The builders may well have been a tribe of giants. Equally mysterious is the purpose of this rounded monolith from 201 Machu Pichu* which was for long believed to have been the scene of the bloody sacrifices of Inca religious ceremonies. It may be more realistic to see in it some kind of solar calendar showing the solstices and giving evidence of very advanced astronomical knowledge.

◄ 199 Peru. Site of Machu Pichu in the Urubamba valley.

201 Machu Pichu. Sculptured monolith known as the 'Observatory of the Sun'.

202 Mexico. The great pyramid, Chichen Itza. Called the 'castillo' by the Spaniards. Its flat roof may have been used for religious ceremonies.

203 Staircase of the great pyramid, Chichen Itza.

Between AD 1000 and 1300 the Mayas (see page 79) experienced some strange fluctuations of fortune. They were quite unaware of the existence of the Incas inhabiting the Andes, as indeed they were of the Europeans or Chinese, and their customs and methods of government belonged to a different world. Their agricultural system never developed beyond the primitive stage. Their instruments remained rudimentary, their methods uncouth and their monuments destined solely for religious purposes. But in spite of some crisis, the exact nature of which we do not know, that split the 'Old Empire' from the new about 925, they maintained and continued to extend their remarkable knowledge of astronomy and to improve their building methods. The earlier towns, such as Palenque, were abandoned, perhaps owing to the exhaustion of the surrounding soil, and the people moved a little further north to the peninsula of Yucatan. Here a complete renaissance of monumental building took place. At Uxmal a great pyramid, similar to the one at Palenque but even steeper, breaks the even line of the horizon; it is ascended by a majestic flight of steps suitable for solemn processions. 'There is nothing crude or barbarous in its proportions and design; the general appearance is, on the contrary,

are trodden by priests, and perhaps by victims.

204 Mexico. Temple of the Warriors, Chichen Itza, seen from the top of the great pyramid.

one of symmetry and grandeur. Were it to stand in the gardens of the Tuileries or in Hyde Park it would be considered worthy of a place beside the ruins of Egyptian, Greek and Roman architecture' (J. L. Stephens). The builders certainly spared no pains in the building of such a monument, for they had to transport five hundred thousand tons of stone on the backs of men. . . .

At Uxmal, however, other influences were already blending with the primitive style, and these are all the more apparent in the great city of the new Maya epoch, at Chichen Itza, to the east of Merida. *Itzas* was the name given by the Mayas to the Toltecs of Mexico.

The great monuments raised here in the Thirteenth Century are the fruit of a union between Maya and Toltec societies, a union which may well have been forced on the former by virtue of conquest. One of the greatest archaeological undertakings of the Twentieth Century, carried out by the Carnegie Institute and the Mexican government, has been to clear and reconstruct these monuments. As all the elements of the buildings remained in place, there was no need to replace any missing part.

At Chichen Itza everything is on the
202 grand scale. The Castillo, the pyramid* which dominates the entire town, reveals curious astronomical affinities: the four
203 staircases* total three hundred and sixty-four steps in all, which, added to the platform itself, makes up the number of days in a year. The temple of the
204 Warriors* is surrounded by an imposing array of sculptured pillars representing soldiers or priests. The white limestone walls are carved into the likeness of innumerable grotesque figures from mythology—serpents, jaguars, vultures. The meaning of the strangest figures, monolithic statues known by their Indian
205 name of Chac Mools*, is a mystery. They are Toltec in origin and represent reclining men, head and knees raised, holding bowl-like receptacles on their abdomens. This is one more facet of the Maya secret, as is the origin of the Toltecs who infused new blood into Maya art. Their capital, Tula (near modern Mexico City), which they abandoned when they migrated to Central America, still guards their secret.

205 *Ibid*. Monolithic statue. Temple of the Warriors.

The giant caryatids of Tula
bear witness to the ambition of a vanished race.

206 Mexico. Caryatid of Tlahuizcalpantecuthli, Tula.

207 *Ibid*. Colossal head. Fragment of a giant caryatid.

208 Mexico. Detail of frieze at the entrance of the Governor's palace, Uxmal.

From the Tenth Century onwards Tula appears to have been the fountain head for all American Indian building, with the exception of the Incas. Sixteen-feet 206 high stone warriors* supported the roof of a massive temple at the foot of a huge, five-stepped pyramid which bears a strange resemblance to the pyramids of Meidum or Saqqara (see page 15). Their 207 giant faces* recall the colossi of Rome or Persepolis, but their grave meditative expressions belong to the native tradition. There is, furthermore, nothing in any of the five continents resembling the geometrical symbolism of the 135-yard long frieze round the temple known as the 208 'Governor's Palace'* at Uxmal (more Toltec than Maya as we have already said). This temple is dedicated to an omnipresent mystical personage, Quetzal-coatl. He was a composite of god, man, bird and snake, and his cult was one of the distinguishing marks of Precolumbian civilisation.

In the Moorish palaces of Spain, stone and water find a perfect synthesis.

In the first days of the year 1492, a very little time before Christopher Columbus discovered the New World, the Moorish king, Boabdil, surrendered his capital of Granada to Ferdinand and Isabella with tears in his eyes. Behind the high walls and the twenty-four towers of the Alcazaba, built by Mohammed I in the Thirteenth Century, their Most Catholic Majesties found the pearl of Andalusia. The palace had been built between 1333 and 1391 by the sultans Yusuf I and Mohammed V, the last heirs of the magnificent traditions of the Almohada supremacy. Its thick, dark-coloured walls dominated the city without appearing to crush it, from the summit of a hill of red sandstone (its name, Alhambra, means red).

The Arabs had been the first people in Europe, from the Eighth Century, to build *alcazars*, palaces with an eye to magnificence, alongside their *alcazabas*, constructed wholly for military purposes. Unfortunately the glittering palaces of Valencia, Toledo, Almeria and, above all, Cordova, have vanished. Our only knowledge of them comes from the enthusiastic descriptions of Arab chroniclers. 'Ten thousand men were constantly at work while the alcazar of Az-Zanra was being built. Fifteen hundred mules and four hundred camels were needed to carry the materials. Six thousand stone blocks were laid each day, not counting the numberless undressed stones. The inlaid ceiling was supported by four thousand, three hundred and twelve marble pillars of many colours, brought from Africa, Greece, France and Italy. The Caliph's audience chamber was entirely of marble. Its walls and ceiling, richly incrusted with precious pearls, diamonds and other gems, were adorned with bas-reliefs and arabesques of exquisite workmanship. And in the centre stood a fountain with a jasper basin, over which twelve life-size animals in solid gold kept watch. . . .'

The Alhambra of Granada did not fall short of this description. The inside was composed of a suite of luxurious apartments, passages, vaulted and painted ceilings, and tracery walls. Twenty-eight pillars made of white marble formed the perfect frame for the Fountain of the
209 Lions*.

This was the axial point of the two palaces which housed the Caliph, his

209 Spain. Court of the Lions, the Alhambra, Granada (31 yds. × 16 yds.). There are 128 marble columns.

warriors state officials and countless servants. All the glittering splendour of the court of the last Muslim kings shone there, around the coteries of poets, artists, scholars, physicians and philosophers. It was these men who had encouraged the building of the Alhambra by setting on foot a general upsurge of cultural life. The Alhambra of Granada formed a link between the fortified castle and the luxurious palace. It set in motion throughout Islam an entirely new interest in glass-blowing and ceramics, as also in planting gardens full of flowers and orange trees. The craft of plumbing

recovered its importance: the Alhambra was a palace of stone and water—water ran in thousands of conduits and small channels, flowing everywhere into fountains whose soothing murmur followed the visitor wherever he went. In this earthly paradise Arab art reached its supreme degree of refinement at the very moment when the power of Islam in Europe was fast waning. Less than a hundred years after so many delicate fabrics and rare skills had been lavished on the creation of the Alhambra of Granada, the palace passed into the hands of new masters.

In India the vimana and the gopuram honour Siva with an exuberance of decoration.

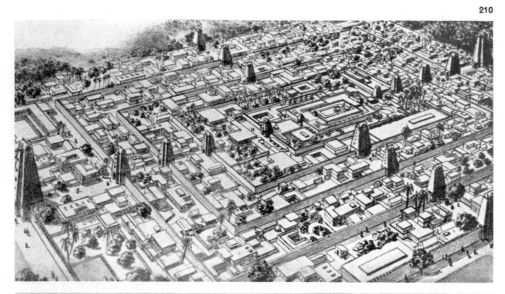

210

210 South India. Reconstruction of the Temple of Sriringam.

211 India. Menaski Temple, Madura. The Gopuram and the city.

211

side to the height of a man, one half buried firmly in the ground and the other rising above it, so that no horseman or foot soldier, be he never so bold, might gain unhindered the outer wall.'

An original monument was to become a symbol of this period of Indian history: the *gopuram*. This was a gigantic door or gateway in the shape of a tower. At Sriringam the roads into the centre of the city passed through twenty-one of them. The *gopuram* was closely related to the *vimana* (see page 91), but these latter, intended to surmount temple sanctuaries, were made up of shallow superimposed terraces whereas the upper storeys of the *gopuram* were habitable and could be reached by stairs. Between the Thirteenth and Seventeenth Centuries the *vimana* diminished in proportion as the *gopuram*, constructed in lighter materials such as brick and wood, rose in height. The shrine remained at the heart of the building, but it came to be

Once it had been driven from Spain and halted outside Vienna, Islam flooded back towards the south-east and in the course of time was to conquer a great deal of India. As they penetrated further south the Muslims came up against the power of the Vijayanagar kings which had grown up as a form of resistance to the invaders. There the last great Brahman temples exalted the centuries-old Dravidian tradition and indicated a fierce determination to protect Hinduism. More and more the cult came to rely on external show. On a set date each year the god travelled through the town, accompanied by great processional chariots: he needed an ever-growing amount of room. One of the most expansive temples to Vishnu in India was at Sriringam*, where the religious precincts enclosed the entire town. Any number of public works were built under the stimulus of religious rivalry which committed whole populations. A dam was built on the Tunghabadra and an aqueduct eleven miles long to carry water to the capital. The traveller might well stand in amazement before a city 'so planned that there were seven fortified walls, one inside another. Beyond the circuit of the outer wall there was an esplanade, about a hundred yards wide, in which stones were set side by

210

212 Dravidian bronze of Siva and Parvati.

213 India. Temple of Kesava, Somnathpur, Mysore. A single hall leads to three temples set round a rectangular central court.

quite dwarfed by the size of gates giving access to it.

After the decline of the Vijayanagar rulers, one small realm dedicated to the worship of Vishnu still survived in the southern tip of India. This was the kingdom of the Nayakas. From 1560 onwards not merely the capital but the whole state of Madura revolved around the temple, over two hundred and fifty yards square, which took a hundred and twenty years to build. One of its nine *gopuram* reached

211 a height of a hundred and fifty feet★. The carvings ran riot over it. There were said to be thirty-three million figures. Inside the temple bronze was as important as stone, and was used to reproduce innumerable groups of the sacred pair,

212 Siva and Parvati★.

True, this exuberance was not new in India. Its only originality lay in adopting higher and higher vertical surfaces for its expression. Three centuries before the present temple, the Hoyshala (of modern Mysore) had been building masterpieces unequalled for the quantity or the quality of their sculptures. The temple of

213 Somnathpur★, built in 1268, was fairly

modest in size and its three identical towers were scarcely thirty feet high, but its star-shaped design allowed ample room for the sculptors to operate. There is not one square inch of stone that has not been

214 utilised★. Geese, elephants (there are said to be eight hundred), mythological creatures, splendidly caparisoned horses, march in procession round the base. There is even one animal depicted unknown in south India: a dromedary with a pair of drums fastened to its flanks which a man is beating vigorously.

At the very period when the full glory of Gothic sculpture had reached its peak in Europe, this stone cavalcade expressed the same unbridled zest, the same sense of the divine presence in everyday life. Now we are coming to the point where all the great works of ecclesiastical architecture in India since the Thirteenth Century were tending to emphasize these feelings, while in Europe the counter-Reformation was breeding an austere, classical style.

214 Somnathpur. Frieze from temple of Kesava.

The heirs of Ghengis Khan
settle down in China and build an imperial city.

216 China. Lu Keow bridge near Pekin (rebuilt in the XVth C.).

The *gopuram* was to become, above all else, the perfect expression of Dravidian India. At Conjeeveram, the *gopuram** is part gateway and part triumphal arch; it is the way into the town and has now been made over to civic purposes.

The Thirteenth Century, which saw the foundations laid of so many great buildings in Europe and America, also witnessed the founding of Pekin. A splendid bridge* takes us across the glassy waters of the Yong-Ting into the Northern Capital. Marco Polo did not see the eleven white arches of marble, which date from the Fifteenth Century when the bridge was rebuilt, but he was extremely impressed with the length of the bridge which was much greater than was usual in Europe. In 1267 Khubla, the grandson of Ghenghis Khan, had decided to build a city on a site which had been inhabited since prehistoric times. He called it Khan Balik, the chief's town. An Arab architect laid out the city according to the chequer-board pattern of the ancient cities of the Han and Sung rulers. To reach their sovereign in the Forbidden City of Purple*, his vassals had to pass through the Chinese city, the Tartar city and the Imperial city. Two hundred thousand labourers* worked on the building of this rigidly planned, four-fold city. Each constituent part of the Forbidden City was known by a symbolic name. The emperor lived in 'the Pavilion of the Clear Sky'.

217 China. Plan of Imperial City of Pekin. Centre: the Forbidden City. XVIIth C. engraving.

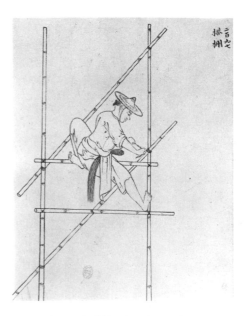

218 Workmen building bamboo scaffolding.

215 India. Conjeeveram. Gopuram now used as a toll-gate.

Guardians in stone keep an enduring watch over the tombs of the Chinese emperors.

220 China. Sung Tombs, Yung Chow ling, Honan. Alley lined with Imperial servants and horses.

The Forbidden City did not long protect the Mongol sovereigns. After 1368 a popular revolution brought into power a dynasty whose roots were truly Chinese: the Ming. Its most famous emperor, Yung-Lo, gave Khan Balik the definitive name of Pei-king and, in 1421, completed simultaneously the Palace of the Examinations and the great temple of Heaven*, a masterpiece in brick and ceramic. The roof, growing progressively smaller towards the top, was a symbol of the protection of the nobles by the celestial powers and of the rule of an *élite* over the bulk of the people. The frequency with which similar roofs recur in Chinese public architecture is an indication of the minutely regulated hierarchy ruling all Chinese society.

The Ming sovereigns devoted equal care to the preparation of their tombs. These were approached by a narrow road lined with awe-inspiring guardians. Many other dynasties had already set the example. There are few sights more striking than the stone groups of horse and rider* which stand in the desolate landscape of Honan province, keeping watch over the tomb of the Emperor Sen Tsung, of the Sung dynasty (1063). There are others though, yet more rugged and forbidding, the lions, horses, camels*, and elephants guarding the path leading to the final resting-place of Yung-Lo. The blocks of marble for these tombs had to be transported in carts with sixteen wheels.

221 China. Ming Tombs near Pekin. Alley lined with camels, elephants and lions.

◄ 219 China. The Temple of Heaven, Pekin.

On the roof of the world pilgrims and monks build the great temple-palace of the Dalai Lamas.

222 Tibet. Lhasa. The Potala, residence of the Dalai Lama on the Red Mountain. 330 yds. long, 490 ft. high, and surrounded by a sacred walk 7½ miles long.

223 Dre Pung: the largest tapestry in the world.

Buddhism found its chosen ground on the roof of the world, where the theocracy of the Dalai Lama established itself. Twelve thousand feet above sea level, Mount Potala dominates Lhasa, the capital of Tibet, and is crowned by the Dalai 222 Lama's winter palace* whose gilded roofs rise thirteen storeys above the sacred esplanade, the Parkhor, commercial centre and heart of the city.

The building, part palace, part monastery, part fortress, was begun in about 1650 on the orders of the fifth Dalai Lama on the site of a much older palace which the Mongols had left in ruins. For years the entire population of Lhasa, men and women, as well as thousands of pilgrims from India and China, carried on their backs the stones to be laid on the gigantic ramparts. The Dalai Lama's sudden death endangered the whole project. Fearing that the volunteers might disperse, the regent decided to conceal the news, with the complicity of a handful of initiates, until the Potala was finished. Rumours were put forth that the Dalai Lama was ill or that he was absorbed in ecstatic meditations. The deception lasted for the ten years required to com-

plete the extraordinary labyrinth of passages and stairways, chambers and chapels which housed thousands of monks. More than a ton of gold, which was brought with great difficulty across the mountains from China, was devoted to the adornment of the bell-turrets; these were already encrusted with precious stones.

Six miles from Lhasa stands an even greater monastery, Dre Pung, which housed seven thousand, five hundred monks and three thousand servants within its massive stone walls. These monks wove the great *tanla*, the largest tapestry 223 in the world*. It is a hundred and ninety-six feet broad and a hundred and thirty feet high, depicts the Buddha in all his glory and is draped on the walls of the Potala on those days when his earthly embodiment appears to the crowds of pilgrims.

Today, when a stranger asks a Tibetan why his countrymen no longer build such monuments he will be told: 'But the Potala is the work of gods, not men. Spirits came and built it during the night. Men could never have achieved such a miracle' (Heinrich Harrer).

Isfahan
and Versailles

the monarchs
as builders

The new aristocrat, the rich banker,
builds palaces as sumptuous as those of any prince.

224 'The building of the Tower of Babel.' Detail of a fresco from the Campo Santo, Pisa, by Benozzo Gozzoli. Builders at work on a XVth C. palace.

On May 30th, 1453, the Turks stormed Constantinople and replaced the cross on the dome of Saint Sophia by the crescent. In the same year the king of France retook Guyenne, and the end of the Hundred Years War was in sight. At both ends of Europe the convulsions of the Middle Ages were subsiding. Islam and Christianity called an uneasy truce. The Feudal era gave place to the nation-state. The new force in the body politic, the great merchant-banker strong enough to influence the election of an emperor and rich enough to eclipse him in the 224 splendour of his palace*, was frequently the one to finance the major building enterprises of the Renaissance. Beside the slaves and the forced labour a new class of workmen had grown up who earned their living as builders. The Sixteenth Century was to see far-reaching changes in the field of construction as a result of social and economic develop-

ments. New inventions, too, such as the hydraulic bellows for furnaces, and a variety of simple mechanisms were gradually reducing the amount of effort required from the labourer. The ship-building industry was also being modernised and the caravels which carried trade to the Far East and to the Americas were constructed in elaborate 225 arsenals such as this one at Barcelona*. Europe perfected a number of Chinese and Arab inventions and was soon building on a scale and with a mastery un-paralleled in the whole world. The architectural advances to which Venice, Rome, London, Madrid, Paris, Versailles were now to bear witness would leave their mark on every land. To an increasing degree the need of a new society to display its wealth in the building of palatial town and country houses was supplementing the demands of religion and of military defence.

225 Spain. Barcelona. Naval shipyard of Atarazanas.

117

The bell-tower stands away from the church.
It symbolises the increased influence of the city fathers.

226 Belgium. Belfry and clock-tower at Tournai.

This belfry in a Flemish city could be either a cathedral tower or the keep of a castle. It marks the transition of power from the Church to the State and from the soldier to the citizen. The word belfry in its original sense meant those wooden towers on wheels with which besieging armies assaulted ramparts, and came initially from the Romans. Then the belfry changed from wood to stone and became a defensive guard tower along frontiers. The third step was when the belfry came to be erected in the centre of a town as a symbol and guarantee of its civic liberty; sometimes it formed part of the town hall, unless, as 226 here*, it stood apart. The bells inside the tower no longer rang for religious services but marked the hours or sounded the alarm. Allowing for local differences, these towers all show a feeling for grandeur at a time when the more ambitious public works tended, as a whole, to evince a preoccupation more with beauty, comfort and careful detail than with sheer size. The vast assemblage of skill, materials and labour was dissipated in thousands of constructions of relatively modest dimensions, though they were as rich in technical ingenuity as the cathedrals and castles of earlier date. The 227 campanile* of St Mark's cathedral is an instance of what fifteenth-century Venice could build on a gigantic scale. All over the city splendid marble-fronted palaces were going up alongside the canals and quays. 'In this dark, afflicted century,' wrote a contemporary, 'she is the only light remaining in hapless Italy.' This was scarcely true. The Renaissance, originating in Florence, where the Duomo and its surroundings testified to the birth of a new style, was manifesting itself through the whole of Italy. Wealthy patrons of the arts vied with one another in ambition and extravagance. At Rome artists like Michelangelo were working for the Popes; the Medicis were transforming Florence; in Milan, where Leonardo da Vinci painted his 'Last Supper', there were the Viscontis and the Sforzas. There were the kings of Aragon at Naples, and the d'Este family in the Duchy of Ferrara, which at this period played the most important part in Italian affairs after Rome and Venice, and where some of Europe's finest town houses were built. A dozen or more architects of genius, eschewing the Gothic style which

227 Italy. Campanile, Piazza San Marco, Venice.

The Leaning Tower is completed and vindicates the faith of its builders.

228 Italy. The Leaning Tower of Pisa. The spiral staircase has 294 steps.

229 Germany. The Holstenthor, Lübeck. Gateway rebuilt in 1477.

had never made much headway in Italy, were attempting to create buildings as ideally proportioned as the human form. The use of a more cohesive mortar in conjunction with brick, wood and tiles allowed the bricklayers and carpenters a considerable degree of flexibility in their work. Not only skill and vision but also obstinacy and perseverance were necessary prerequisites of the builders. When work was already well advanced on the campanile at Pisa the building began to tilt alarmingly, owing to a subsidence in the soil, and the City Fathers decided to abandon the structure. Giovanni di Simone, however, did fresh calculations and concluded that work could continue; he instilled new confidence in his masons and among the entire population. By 1350 the leaning tower* was finished. This hundred-and-sixty-foot campanile, with its colonnaded outside staircase ascending it in a graceful spiral, is one of the most important architectural features of the century.

But at the end of the Middle Ages the love of art was far from being the only inspiration of urban architecture in Europe. The strong wall and the well-fortified gateway still gave some measure of security to the towns of the West even though progress in the art of destruction was threatening to limit the practical utility of massive bastions such as this gateway at Lübeck*, rebuilt in 1477, which shows the insecurity felt by all the cities of the Hanseatic League in a storm-ridden Germany. This federation of the principal ports of North-western Europe forged the most effective instrument of commercial and political co-operation known up to that time.

The kings of France
transform their castles in the Italian image.

230 France. Château of Chambord, Loire-et-Cher. Length of façade: 164 yds. Breadth: 123 yds. 365 chimneys. A wall 20 miles long surrounds the park.

231 *Ibid*. Double spiral staircase.

The supremely palatial style of architecture, like that which characterises the 230 Château de Chambord*, was a direct result of the French kings' Italian campaigns. Charles VIII of France fell in love with the lands he passed through south of the Alps and harvested all their secrets of art and beauty. He brought home with him one sculptor, two architects, a gardener and a dozen craftsmen. This was a period when all the rulers of Europe were vying to steal artists and craftsmen from one another. The King of England recruited miners from Hungary, the Tsar Ivan the Terrible had Danish printers and English metalworkers. The same demand for their services took glass-makers, engravers, weavers, tapestry workers, and engineers from country to country.

All these skills were brought together in the Loire Valley, thanks to the demands of a king who had ample means to indulge his enthusiasm and curiosity for whatever was new and strange. The great Renaissance châteaux grew and multiplied in this region. It became the principal seat of the French monarchy and included among its glories Loches, Chaumont, Amboise (1492–1510); Blois; parts of Chenonceaux (1513–1521) and Azay-le-Rideau (1518–1524). All the traditional military defences, moats, towers and the like, were still in evidence, but their use now was purely decorative.

François I spent lavishly to increase the standing of the Valois dynasty. In 1519 he began to build Chambord in the centre of a huge area of parkland twenty miles round. He planned to divert the Loire so that it would flow at the foot of the château, but the enormity of the task discouraged him. None the less Chambord took fifteen years to build. A

120

From the builder's practice, the theories of architecture are developed in all their complexity.

disegno
I. terzo ordine di questo Palazzo segnato in questo al profilo A. ancorche tutto questo piano, ouero ultimo ordine non e dissimile a questo luogo, il quale hà nel mezzo il Coritore B. che uolta, intorno per seruitio di so-camere, essendo il C per la fila di r. di quelle, con 40. mezzane di sopra il D per l'altra fila delle 23 altre camere, con otto porte comune, che escono sopra la loggia circolare. E. Canale denzo la grossezza del muro per riceuere, et condurre l'acqua fuori del Palazzo. F. Coritore largo di 10. palmi, porato sopra gli archi nell'. interiore del muro, il qual coperto per non esser fatta la balaustrata. G. Canne di tutti li camini del Palazzo. H. Torre del Palazzo minore che l'disegno dell'Architetto. Altezza principale di questo Palazzo palmi 120. per l'alzeza di tutto il Palazzo, cioè de 1 piano del Cortile, à K sopra l'ultima Cornice palmi 80. per l'altre, cui de due ordine del Cortile.

232 Geometry. Detail, tomb of Pope Sixtus IV.

233 Italy. Section of the pentagonal palace at Caprarola, the masterpiece of the architect Vignola. Today it is the Italian president's summer residence.

work force of eighteen hundred was employed on the task, which was complicated by the marshy nature of the soil. The castle, preserving its medieval plan and enormous keep, is simply a stone cube fifty yards square surmounted by decorative adornments after the Italian fashion. It is said that Leonardo da Vinci contributed his advice, especially in the design of the double spiral stair-
231 case★. The question is debatable but it is certain that this type of staircase, found in many buildings of the period, is one example of the increased importance
232 assigned to geometry★ in architecture. Geometrical considerations were to become a guiding principle not only in the purely technical aspects of the craft but also—sometimes with quite a startling effect—in the aesthetic conception of a building.

The famous pentagonal palace built by

233 the architect Vignola at Caprarola★ was to start a fashion. 'I have seen no palace in all Italy to equal it,' wrote Montaigne. 'It has a great moat around, cut into the rock; the building rises above it like a terrace in such a way that the roof-tiles are invisible. There are five corners but it appears to the eye as a square. Within, the plan is circular, with broad curving corridors arched and painted all over. The rooms are all square. The building is of great size.'

The profession of architect took a decisive step forward at this time. There was no longer anything in common between the foreman, a humble workman who was always present at the site and who was still treated on the same level as carters and water carriers in the Vatican in 1460, and these men, respected masters of their advanced technical
234 knowledge★.

234 Two architects, by Maso da San Friano.

Ivan the Terrible looks to Italy,
and to Islam, for the adorning of his capital.

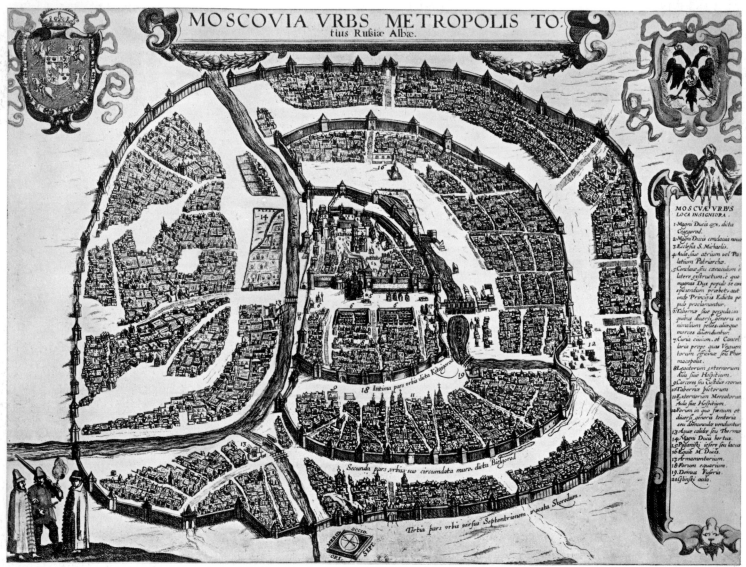

235 Plan of XVIIth C. Moscow.

237 Moscow. Cathedral of Saint Basil (detail of the domes).

Ivan the Terrible came to the throne in 1533, the same year that the Château de Chambord was completed. The replacement of the innumerable wooden buildings which had grown up over six centuries with edifices built of stone transformed Moscow from the centre of a modest principality into the capital of a 235 powerful state*. The Milanese Marco Friazini and Pietro Solari enlarged and rebuilt the central citadel, the Kremlin, in collaboration with the Russian architects of Pskov, Vladimir and Novgorod. The Kremlin retained its original untidy lay-out, while acquiring a host of new churches, palaces and monuments. In the central square the venerable cathedral of 236 the Assumption*, where the coronation of the Tsars took place, blended Re-

naissance ornamentation with traditional Russian elements. In front of the cathedral was the Ivan Veliky tower, completed by Boris Godunov in 1600, surmounted by its gigantic gold cross rising three hundred and twenty-five feet into the air, which Napoleon never succeeded in bringing back to Paris. At the foot of the tower is the biggest bell in the world, the *Tsar Kolokhoi*. It weighs two hundred tons, is said to be large enough to accommodate two hundred men, and fell from its belfry during the fire of 1737.

But the most stupendous work of all the Russias lies outside the Kremlin walls, in Red Square. This is Saint Basil's cathe-237 dral*. The architect, an Italian, is said to have been blinded by order of the Tsar to prevent him from repeating his feat.

236 Russia. The Cathedral of the Assumption, Moscow. ➤

St Peter's basilica consecrates the glory of the papacy but hastens the split of Christendom.

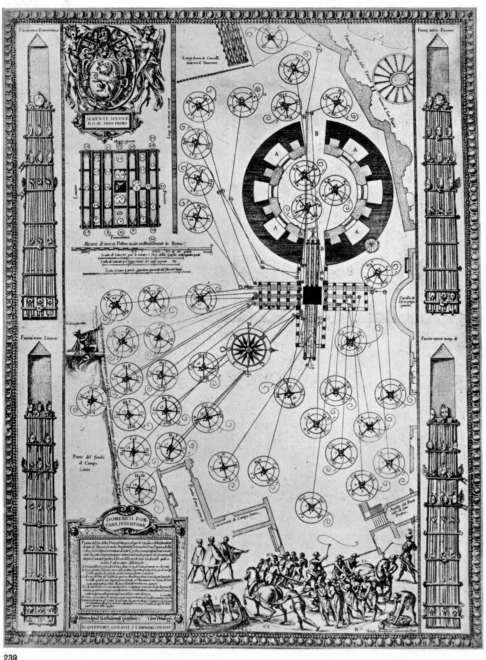

239

240

239 Raising the obelisk before St Peter's: the winches.

240 England. St Paul's Cathedral, London. XVIIIth C. engraving.

In 1555 Michelangelo presented Pope Paul IV with the model of the dome that was to crown the new basilica dedicated to Saint Peter in Rome*. Almost exactly half a century earlier, on April 18th, 1506, Pope Julius II had laid the foundation stone of the building, which was not to be finally consecrated until 1626. Bramante had demolished the nave of the original basilica, dating from the Fourth Century, and begun the gigantic new church, planned in the form of a Greek cross with four short, equal arms, and destined to cover an area amounting to a total of at least twenty-five thousand square yards.

Raphael was the next director of operations, and after his premature death he was succeeded by Sangallo and Peruzzi. When Michelangelo died in 1565, the dome was still far from being finished. Afterwards Vignola, Ligorio and Nanni di Baccio Bigio, then G. della Porta all worked on the basilica; it was under Fontana that the dome reached its full height: four hundred and thirty-five feet.

Paul V's architect, Maderno, completely changed Bramante's design and gave the basilica the form of a Latin cross terminating in the broad façade overlooking Saint Peter's Square. It was left for Bernini to erect the baldaquin, ninety-five feet high, over the High Altar, and then, in the eleven years between 1656 and 1667, to put up the two hundred and eighty-four columns bounding the approach. One of the most delicate operations in all the history of the building was the removal of the obelisk of Caligula which had stood beside the original basilica, and its re-erection in the centre of the square. This was carried out in absolute silence by hundreds of workmen, manning dozens of winches*.

The whole of the Christian world took part in the building of the new church by virtue of a large-scale system of financing, one of whose aspects, the sale of indulgences, was to be an indirect cause of the Reformation. Imitations of St Peter's sprang up in all parts of the world and even the Capitols of American cities are based on it. Another building inspired by it is Wren's masterpiece, Saint Paul's Cathedral in London*.

◄ 238 Michelangelo presenting a model of Saint Peter's to Pope Paul IV.

125

The thirst for precious metals turns mining into a major industry.

241 Spain. Rio Tinto, Andalusia, where copper and iron pyrites are found. Here: quarrying manganese ore.

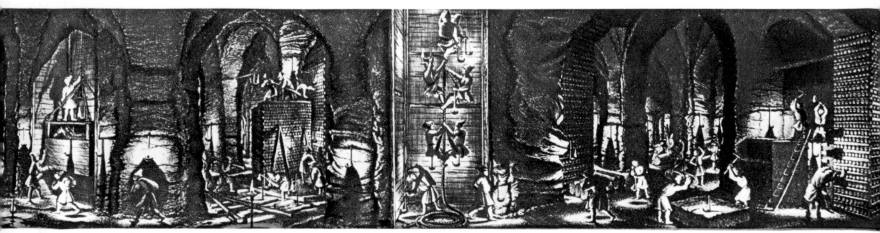

244 Poland. Salt mines at Wieliczka, near Cracow.

242 Section drawing of XVIth C. mine.

243 Mining gold and silver in Spanish America. XVIth C.

The dome of St. Paul's would fit several times over into this enormous open-cast
241 mine at Rio Tinto★, near Seville. It was begun in classical times, and even today it still produces over half the world's supplies of iron and copper pyrites. From the end of the Middle Ages the Hapsburgs gained much of the wealth which lay behind their political power from working some of the most valuable silver-seams in Europe. The mining zones of Germany, in the mountains of Saxony, Bohemia and Silesia, as well as in Styria and Carinthia were yielding substantial quantities of copper, lead, iron and silver. In places like Augsburg, Leipzig and Nuremberg the local rulers would farm out rights in the extraction and exploitation of mining products to the rich burghers of the town.

Typical of this early form of capitalism was Jacob Fugger, who was responsible for the election of Charles V as Emperor, in 1519, thanks to the unparalleled power obtained from his mining interests: gold from Reichenberg, silver from the Tyrol, copper from Hungary and Thuringia.

In 1526 Hochstetter became the 'mercury king' and was to gain entire control of the minting of coinage in western Europe. Thirty years later Georges Bauer, who controlled the mines belonging to the town of Chemnitz, published, under the pseudonym Agricola, a work entitled *De re metallica*. The book was illustrated with examples of mining at this period, when the growing demand for metals drove the miners in search of
242 ever deeper seams★.

Mechanisation had already been intro-

duced to some extent in order to increase the yield and at the same time lessen the risks involved. There were bucket and chain systems, ventilation bellows, air pipes fed by windmills, outsize winches.

Voluntary labour was recruited in increasing quantity and rewarded by attractive privileges. Their conditions formed a great contrast to those in the
243 mines of the New World★ where the Indians were pressed into service as forced labour. It must be admitted, however, that parts of Europe were little better. In Poland, for instance, the mines
244 of Wieliczka★ were worked by a plentiful supply of serfs and convicts. Intensive excavation often turned the salt mines into complete cities six hundred feet underground; the refining of the salt
245 took place on the surface★.

245 Wieliczka. Surface installations. Refining and despatching the salt in the early XVIIIth C.

246 Spain. Monastery of San Lorenzo del Escorial, near Madrid.

None of the great works of the Renaissance would have been possible without this abundance of precious metals. From 1545 onwards, some hundred thousand Peruvian natives were employed, whether they liked it or not, digging galleries at Potosi and keeping six thousand furnaces heated on llama dung in order to ensure a constant flow of silver into Spain. Political power and influence was passing into new hands. Spain, who held the source of gold and silver, and England, France and Holland who dealt in these metals, were coming to the fore. It was when Spain was at her wealthiest and most influential that she achieved her most ambitious feat of building—the monastery of the Escurial, built some thirty miles from Madrid between 1567 and 1584. The splendid façade of the Escurial★ rose at the foot of the Sierra Guadarrama on a plateau scored with iron workings. The monument, built by order of Philip II★, expressed the subtle blend of religious faith and royal ambition characteristic of his reign and of the period itself, torn by the wars of religion.

The Escurial's history reflects its times. While Philip was at war with France he bombarded Saint Quentin and destroyed the church of St Lawrence. To make amends and also in gratitude for his victory, he vowed to build a monument to the martyred saint in the shape of the gridiron on which he died★. It was to be an enormous monastery, residence of the kings of Spain during their lifetime and resting-place after their deaths.

For twenty-three years a brilliant architect, Herrera, pitted himself against the grey-blue granite of the Sierra Guadarrama (and against the fractious temperament of the Spanish labourers) to satisfy the king's whim. He wrote fifty chapters of meticulous instructions for the discipline of the workmen and the ordering of materials. He invented cranes and

247 Coin of Philip II of Spain. Bibl. Nat.

248 The Escurial. Main entrance and church. XVIIth C. engraving.

248

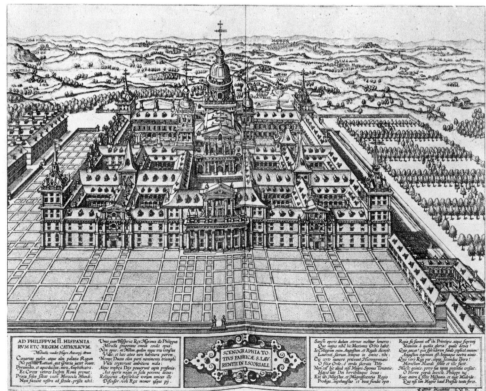

Austere at home, the Spaniards in Latin America evolve the exuberant fashion of 'Colonial Baroque'.

249 Ecuador. Jesuit Church at Quito in Colonial Baroque style.

250 Mexico. Ceiling of Dominican church at Oaxaca. The vine of Jesse.

machines to haul the blocks to the site, for in spite of the opposition of the monks, these were shaped in the actual quarry as they had been in ancient Egypt. Special carts drawn by forty pairs of oxen were needed to move the stones for the main gateway. When the work was half finished Philip suddenly decided to double the number of monks and to add a college and a seminary to the establishment. Faced with the necessity to enlarge the Escurial, Herrera ignored the advice of those who suggested increasing the overall area of the monastery and added, instead, a second floor. When the great work was finished the king and his architect were exhausted. The building comprised no fewer than sixteen courts, eleven hundred

outside windows, sixteen hundred interior windows, twelve hundred doors and eighty-six staircases. Philip II had given free rein to his morbid delight in supervising, as Cheops had done, the creation of his own dazzlingly splendid tomb.

Spain at this time was covering the Americas with a network of monastic houses, initially fortified; with churches, which were often built on the sites of Indian temples; and with chapels, new towns, plantations, *estancias*, *haciendas* and mining installations. The façade of the 249 Jesuit church at Quito★, or the tree of life painted on the ceiling of the one at 250 Oaxaca★ are among the many examples of the exuberance and originality of the 'Colonial Baroque' style which spread

over a vast area, blending elements of European Baroque and local artistic traditions. These buildings are far from the severity of the Escurial, and understandably so when we remember that Spain sent no artists on the heels of the conquistadors, but only craftsmen, masons, carpenters, or stone-workers, whose mission it was to teach the rudiments of their crafts to the native labourers and then to employ them as far as possible. The natives may have been put to work on a building of Spanish design, but they would carry it out in Indian fashion, often producing brilliant recreations of the exuberant adornments of their own temples. Thus the vanquished took their revenge on their conquerors.

Order and symmetry preside
over the creation of the Renaissance garden.

251 Germany. Castle and gardens at Heidelberg. Right: the town beside the river Neckar.

252 Japan. Garden of Ryoan-ji, Kyoto. The rocks may represent the Japanese archipelago.

With the age of the fortified castles behind chem, and enriched by the wealth of new discoveries as also by plentiful gold and silver, the people of Europe turned with zest to the improvement of Nature. The Renaissance garden has its roots in a tradition which traced its origins back to Ancient Rome through Byzantium and the Moorish occupation of Spain. The first European park laid out to an architectural design was a project of Bramante's for the Vatican gardens in 1503. The two centuries that followed were to see the gardens of western Europe reach an astonishing pitch of elegance and beauty. An effect

251 such as that at Heidelberg* could only be obtained with considerable means and a real genius for design. Terraces, arbours and geometrical patterns made one with the castle and the houses of the town.

At the other end of Asia at this period there was a similar fashion for the formal garden. The art of the Chinese garden had passed to Japan through Korea, but the

Water, too, is made obedient
to the endless inventiveness of the Italian architect.

Japanese added to it their own strict code of rules, making of the garden a world in miniature. The entire nation took pride in its gardens, and every temple, every rich merchant's or noble's home would be embellished with a garden of tasteful simplicity, like the stone garden of Ryoan-ji at Kyoto* which was designed to be gazed at by the contemplative rather than to be walked in by the stroller. From the Thirteenth Century Zen Buddhism had spread from China to the *élite* of Japan. Its highest expression lay in intellectual and spiritual concentration. Here the white sand symbolises pure reality and the small furrows stand for the waves of the sea. Fifteen rocks are arranged in five groups according to certain aesthetic and philosophical premises and in such a way that only fourteen of them can be seen at one glance; they represent the islands of Japan.

Water is the dominant element in the Sixteenth Century gardens of the Villa d'Este at Tivoli*. Their architect, Ligorio, took advantage of the steep hillside sloping away from the villa to create a garden on five narrow terraces, all watered by fountains, cascades and glassy pools. He also installed water-powered automata*. The fashion for these ingenious comical mechanisms was to spread from Italy into every court in Europe.

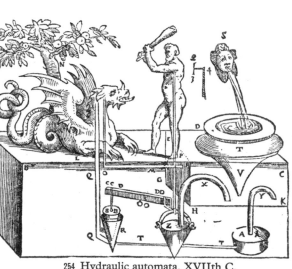

254 Hydraulic automata. XVIIth C.

253 Italy. Villa d'Este, Tivoli, near Rome. Fountain and water organ.

The domes and minarets of Islam set their seal on Constantinople.

255 Turkey. Blue Mosque of the Sultan Ahmed Cami, Istanbul. There are six minarets, a central cupola and four half-domes.

SVLIMANO IMPERATOR DE TVRCHI

After its conquest by the Turks, Constantinople became the capital of Islam. The city was now donning her Islamic dress, created by artisans who were either captured or drawn there by the promise of great rewards. Not content with turning St Sophia into a mosque, the sultans, between 1609 and 1616, built another mosque to rival it on the other side of the remains of the Hippodrome, on the site of the imperial palaces. It was called the 255 Mosque of the Sultan Ahmed*, or Blue Mosque, and was the largest and finest in the world. Pilgrims assembled there for the first stage of their long journey to Mecca. But the Imam of Mecca could not forgive the Sultan Ahmed for surrounding the new mosque with six minarets, a privilege hitherto reserved for the Kaaba. Now the Imam felt compelled to build a

seventh (see page 82). The striking characteristic from which the Blue Mosque derived its name was the decoration of the inner walls, covered all over as far as the topmost windows with tiles 256 predominantly blue and green*. It was the greatest achievement in ceramics the world had ever seen and gave evidence of the pinnacle reached in this art by the Turkish Empire after the conquests of 257 Suleiman the Magnificent*. The 're-builder of the Roman Empire in the name of Allah' as he was called, extended his reign over three-quarters of the Ancient world, and spread his taste for extravagant luxury from Egypt to Morocco, from Hungary to the Crimea.

257 Suleiman the Magnificent. Engraving.

256 Central hall of the Blue Mosque. (The kneeling figures indicate the scale.) ➤

At Isfahan the Shah builds
great works to rival those of the Sultan.

The gilded dome of the sanctuary of Fatima at the Persian holy town of Qumm* seems like an echo of that of the mosque of Ahmed. This was still Sixteenth Century Islam and the Safarid dynasty ruled in Iran. At this time the Sunnites of Constantinople and the Shiites of Persia were engaged in religious strife as murderous as that which was tearing Christendom. The Turkish sultans' worst enemy, against whom they mobilised their largest armies and because of whom they were unable to penetrate into Europe further than Vienna, was the Shah of Persia, their brother in religion. The Shah Abbas the Great, a contemporary of Queen Elizabeth, was a fine figure of a man with a luxuriant moustache. Tired of roving from place to place with his train of seven thousand camels carrying his tents, furnishings, carpets, gold vessels, provisions, and also the leaden pipes and fountains which were laid out to form his garden each evening, he decided to found Isfahan. Before long the new city was graced with the five-storeyed, throne-shaped Ali Qapu, or High Gate, with its audience chamber whose ceiling was composed of a meticulous arrangement of cavities designed to improve the acoustics*. In order to water his gardens Abbas II diverted the waters of the Zenderhud with a dam surmounted by a graceful bridge* of twenty-four arches. Masonry and hydraulic engineering enabled the famous roses of Isfahan to bloom.

259 Iran. Ceiling in the pavilion of Ali Qapu, Isfahan.

260 Isfahan. Bridge over the Zenderhud at Khadiu. Twenty-four arches set on piers which can be used to form a dam.

◄ 258 Iran. Inner court of the shrine of Fatima, Qumm.

To the glory of Vishnu of the thousand incarnations, the Jain Buddhists raise a city of a thousand temples.

261 India. Sacred city of Satrunyaya, Palitana, containing nearly nine hundred Jain temples.

261 The Muslim tide also flowed over a part of India and left its mark on the great works of construction, even though Jainism, the oldest form of Hindu faith, maintained its hold in many parts of the land. Its towns show the tenacious hold of tradition. Satrunyaya*, the holiest of Jain temple-cities, contains no fewer than nine hundred religious buildings. Most of them were built after the Eleventh Century, when the first Muslim invasion had left not a stone standing. The rich business men of Rajastan, however, were faithful to the religion of their ancestors and, taking advantage of the tolerance

which soon followed the fanaticism of the first Mogul rulers, they set about extensive rebuilding in the Sixteenth Century and onwards. They reproduced the original style but brought to it new elements. An imposing proliferation of shrines—cupolas, cones, pyramids—dedicated to Vishnu and attendant deities, were grouped inside walled enclosures.

During his long reign, from 1556–1605, Akbar, a descendant of Tamerlane, extended the rule of the Grand Moguls over the whole of north India. He left the richest empire in the world, covered with new cities and monuments. In an effort to

surpass him, his grandson, Shah Jahan, spent all this huge fortune on raising monuments of unparalleled splendour. The most famous of them is the Taj
262 Mahal* at Agra, the result of the labours of Hindu, Turkish, Persian, Venetian and French architects. It was built in response to the dying wish of the Grand Mogul's favourite wife, to provide a tomb worthy of their love. To build it Shah Jahan gathered together twenty thousand men. Work progressed from 1630 to 1653 and resulted in the most famous of all Indian monuments, made entirely of white marble set with coloured

262 India. The Taj Mahal, Agra. White marble tomb of Shah Jahan's wife. 192 ft. high.

stones and flanked by four minarets a hundred and thirty feet high. The mausoleum itself is nearly two hundred feet wide and its onion-dome rises to the equivalent height. The perfect harmony of the whole is heightened by the gardens surrounding it, in which green cypress alleys alternate with lines of fountains and ponds. The extravagant Shah Jahan intended to match it with a twin mausoleum for his own tomb, this time in black marble, but his son, Aurungzebe, appalled at the ruin with which this plan threatened the treasury, saw no alternative but to depose and imprison his father. Today, therefore, the Taj Mahal rises in splendid isolation.

A few years later the same Aurungzebe, in the course of extending Akbar's conquests, seized a brand new monument which was one of the most ambitious in all the East. This was the Gol Gumbad★, built in 1660 as a tomb for the Sultan Mohammed Adil Shah. It was a perfect cube, the same size as the Taj Mahal, crowned with a dome a hundred and forty feet in diameter—almost the same dimensions as the dome of Saint Peter's.

263 India. Gol Gumbad. Mausoleum of Sultan Mohammed Adil Shah.

Ships from all over the globe
sail up the Thames to London Bridge.

264 England.   Panoramic view of London in 1650.   North bank: St Paul's to the Tower.   South bank (foreground): Southwark.   London Bridge was

The volume of international trade was augmented by Europe's overseas explorations. Powerful commercial enterprises grew up in England, France and, especially, Holland to trade with the East and West Indies. The existing ports were developed in order to meet the need to accommodate increased traffic and tonnage.

Hamburg, Bordeaux and Lisbon grew in importance. Amsterdam, which had been entirely reclaimed from the sea in the course of three centuries of unremitting toil, was the site of a royal palace built on 13,659 piles. Ten docks were built at Rotterdam deep enough to enable ships to moor directly opposite the merchant's houses. Stockholm, at the centre of an archipelago of ten thousand islands, grew in thirty years from a population of eight thousand to one of forty thousand. This was an age of

expansion particularly for the river ports, situated well inland and capable of handling the heaviest cargoes.

The invention of the lock, already in use for a century or so, had enabled the French to open the Briare canal and later the Languedoc canal, just as it had enabled Holland to develop her system of canals to keep pace with her importance as a commercial power. Antwerp became a stake in the commercial rivalry between England, France and Holland.

264   London* was the prime example of all the development of the great ports at this time. The city was still medieval, imprisoned in a strait-jacket of twisting, evil-smelling lanes and difficult of access by road, but new docks were being built along the Thames-side and the flow of world trade into the city was on the increase. This contrast between the city and the port was analogous to the general

situation of an Old World not yet attuned to the spate of new discoveries and techniques. It is impossible to say what solution London would have found had it
265   not been for the Great Fire* which started on September 2nd, 1666, and for five days wrought havoc in the world's largest wooden city. No tyrant would have dared set about clearing and cleansing the city on the vast scale of the fire which destroyed thirteen thousand houses and ninety churches, though taking only twelve lives.

Regrettably the city was not rebuilt as it might have been. Christopher Wren, a young scholar turned architect, who was already well known for his work at Oxford and Cambridge, drew up, in two weeks, a revolutionary plan in the grand Italian manner, with broad boulevards and spacious quays. King Charles II gave the plan his enthusiastic support, but the

London is harried by fire,
but its prosperity comes to it by water.

at this time the only bridge over the Thames.

city shopkeepers put up a stubborn resistance to it. All they wanted was to rebuild their premises on the old sites. As a result the new London merely reproduced the medieval labyrinth. The only change was the use of stone instead of wood and a slight improvement in access to the port. A great scheme was thwarted by the united opposition of individuals.

But at least Wren was allowed to rebuild St Paul's cathedral (see page 125) and the fifty churches whose white spires rise above the huddle of low, brown-tiled roofs. Wren's design for St Paul's was similar to Bramante's for St Peter's in Rome, a Greek cross, but the plan was not carried out here either. The Court faction, which was looking forward to the restoration of the Roman Catholic faith, insisted on a long nave with side chapels as being more suitable for services in the Roman rite.

265 The Great Fire of London, 1666.

Louis XIV builds Versailles
and affirms the power of the monarchy in France.

266 The Aqueduct of Maintenon. Picture commemorating 'the magnificent achievements of Louis the Great'.

In the autumn of 1668 three friends made a memorable visit to the most famous site of the Seventeenth Century. Boileau, La Fontaine and Racine went to Versailles. Madame de Sévigné, too, was in the habit of taking her friends from the provinces out to see it. Trippers, even then, flocked to Versailles from Paris, from northern France and from the Midi, indeed from all over the world. The Sun-King had chosen as the site for his royal palace a marshy tract of land with nothing to recommend it, without even a stream.

All France, nevertheless, began singing the praises of Louis XIV's architectural

266 genius*. 'If a single bolt is broken, his Majesty is displeased,' wrote the Minister Colbert. The king inspected everything down to the last detail almost daily from 1661, when work on the building began, to May 6th, 1682, when he moved into the palace—'withdrawing the court from Paris for ever', said Saint-Simon. Nothing would discourage him, neither the unhealthy mists rising off the marshes, which gave him fever and decimated the workmen, nor the terrible winters of 1678 to 1684 when masons and stone-cutters, most of whom came from the Limousin, much further south, deserted

every day 'even when they were owed two weeks' pay'. Louis was not even to be discouraged by financial difficulties, though in 1688 he had to sell his own silver plate in order to continue the work.

Nothing daunted, Louis, cane in hand, would tour the site, picking his way amid the scaffolding, the pulleys, ladders, piles of stone and forests of beams, amid the tumbrils and drays drawn by more than six thousand horses; he would stop to talk to some of the thirty-six thousand workers engaged on the building. Many of these were poor devils dragged from the four corners of France to toil on the immense foundations, but many others were distinguished craftsmen who were on an equal social footing with the king's stewards. These were the decorators, gilders, wood carvers, bronze-sculptors, a host of artisans supervised by the architect Le Vau (who began the work), the painter Le Brun, and the gardener Le Nôtre, with his big black apron, who was responsible for the vast panorama of gardens and fountains. Finally there was Mansard, the architect who took over the work and carried it to completion.

267 An aerial view* of this embodiment of the absolute monarchy that ruled France during the *Grand Siècle* shows how complete their victory was. Louis XIII's earlier 'house of cards' was embedded, 'like a truffle in some fabulous pâté' within the huge establishment housing the king and his thirty thousand courtiers for whom Paris was becoming too small. Three broad avenues fanned out from the front of the palace towards St Cloud, Paris and Sceaux, through the town of Versailles which underwent development of the same time. A whole army of workmen and soldiers laid 'the King's Way' from Versailles to the capital, the most sumptuous road since Roman times. A technician of Arab origin called René Rennequin Sualem evolved the *machine*
268 *de Marly** in order to draw water from the Seine, carry it up a gradient and down into the park. A reservoir was built at Louveciennes, above Marly, where fourteen hydraulic wheels, each forty feet in diameter, were installed to work 221 pumps which drew up six thousand cubic metres of water every twenty-four hours. This hydraulic machine had a capacity equal to two hundred horsepower, an incredible amount for that period. The machine was so finely adjusted that it ran

267 France. Versailles, showing the three avenues, the royal stables, the courtyard, the palace and the gardens.

from 1682 until 1804 without a single break, and was then overhauled and ran until 1861. Over twelve miles of timber had gone into its installation. An ambitious attempt to carry the waters of the Eure to Versailles across an aqueduct had to be abandoned as a result of war and terrible epidemics of fever. Altogether a sum equivalent to twenty-nine million pounds or eighty-one million dollars today went into the building of Versailles. The palace, in its superb gardens, was perhaps the ultimate show-piece of autocratic monarchy; before the power of the throne was to be shaken to its foundations, it found its symbolic expression in a building of unparalleled magnificence. Subsequent palaces might equal, but never surpass this one built by Louis XIV.

268 The Marly pumps taking water from the Seine. XVIIth C. engraving.

The Maharajah of Jaipur builds
for prestige; the façade must come first.

270 India. Jaipur. The Hawa Mahal, or House of the Winds. This is, in fact, only a façade.

At the opposite end of the globe, Akbar had anticipated Louis XIV. He had begun Fatpur Sikri* in 1570 with the idea of fusing the Muslim and Hindu faiths. He did at least achieve an architectural synthesis of the two styles in a vast assemblage of palaces, mosques and tombs built on a huge plateau of red sandstone, surrounded by a fortified wall with great gates in it, and overlooking an artificial lake. But lack of water reduced Akbar's dream to nothing.

In the period of decadence that followed in India there would be no more than a few isolated undertakings by petty princes. One of these, Jai Singh, the Maharajah of Jaipur, also had an ambition to found a new, regularly planned city. The plan included this bizarre 'House of the Winds'* which was never more than an isolated façade. Jai Singh also developed a passionate interest in astronomy. First he had five observatories built at Delhi, then at Benares and Jaipur*, where he replaced the bronze instruments, such as the astrolabe which he thought was inaccurate, by gigantic instruments of marble and red sandstone invented by himself. These include the *Samrat Yantra*, for measuring solar time, the *Ram Yantra*, for calculations in astronomy, and the *Jai Prakash Yantra*, built to demonstrate that the earth is round. They are all remarkably accurate.

271 India. Jaipur. The observatory: instruments made of red sandstone and white marble.

269 India. Fatpur Sikri, near Agra. Courtyard of the Mosque and Gate of Victory. ➤

Greater ornamentation and greater bulk
mark the development of the temples of Siam.

In their capital city, Ayuthia, founded in 1351 on the north side of the Menam delta in rich rice-growing land, the Thais had built a number of the great double aisled temples, known as *wat*. One aisle was reserved for the ordination of monks and for important functions, while the other was set aside for preaching and for religious ceremonies. Both of them led up to a statue of Buddha. The largest of these Buddhas*, in the *wat* Mongolpitra, is one of the finest in all Asia. It shows one characteristic feature of Thai art, which is the vertical tendency of the buildings and statues. Although the Buddha is seated in an attitude of enlightment, right hand extended downwards as though calling the earth to witness his triumph—he seems almost as tall as if he were standing, such is the effect of the elongation of his face culminating in a point of flame.

The *stupas* (see page 54) dominating the great temple of Bangkok* also follow this tendency towards elongation and almost develop into spires. The rich, colourful decoration of the temple, with its shades of gold, blue and violet, is an indication of the city's power. It was founded in 1782, right in the heart of the Menam delta after Ayuthia had been taken by the Burmese.

Bangkok was planned on strictly functional lines. In the centre: an island surrounded by a canal and given over entirely to the royal palace and government buildings, without a single private dwelling. In the middle of that, another canal marked off the quarter where the palace of the rulers rose among huge court-yards surrounded by stores. Lying outside this nucleus and bounded by a third canal concentric with the first two was the religious quarter, with pagodas, monasteries and gardens, and the residential area, the one to the north, the other to the south. The whole city bore the marks of a strong, centralised government.

Here we take leave of Asia for a long period. The monuments of Pekin will be improved and others, such as the wonderful Summer Palace, will be built. But in the Nineteenth Century neither China nor India are to build anything on a scale comparable to the immensity of the continent of Asia.

272 Thailand. Colossal bronze Buddha at Ayuthia.

273 Thailand. The temple of the Emerald Buddha. Bangkok.

**Versailles starts a fashion
for the geometric, for the outsize.**

274

275

274 Morocco. Meknes. Bab-Mansur Gate.

275 Jules Hardouin-Mansard.

276 Sweden. Royal Summer Palace, Drott-
ningholm.

276

277 Spain. Royal Palace, Madrid. East front: 150 yds. long and 106 ft. high.

For many years to come other European princes were to be lured by Louis XIV's example of sumptuous architecture. Even the Moroccan tyrant, Moulay Ismail, who was a great admirer of the Sun King endowed his new capital of Meknes with magnificent palaces and built there the monumental gateway of Bab-Mansur el-Aleuj*, named after the renegade Christian supposed to have designed it.

274

Lunéville, Caserta, Potsdam—all over Europe royal palaces arose under the sign of Versailles.

The architect importance achieved an he

was never to reach again. In France the chief of them all was Jules Hardouin-Mansard*, who came into his own when Louis XIV entrusted him with full power to complete Versailles. He was too late to influence the design of the charming Summer Palace of the Swedish kings, at Drottningholm*, which was begun in 1661. Its site was an island in Lake Malaren and its architect, a Frenchman named Tessin the elder, modelled it on Le Vau's original Versailles. But it was Mansard who gave the impression of having rebuilt Versailles

275

276

on a hill overlooking Madrid, in 1734, after the Alcazar* had been burned down. Napoleon was to tell his brother, Joseph, when he made him King of Spain: 'Brother, you are better housed than I am!'

277

The new palace of Schönbrunn* was built by Fischer von Erlach in a style modelled on Versailles, the old schloss having been burned down during the Turkish siege of 1683. The park, adorned with statues and fountains and crowned by a belvedere, was laid out in the French manner after the formula of Le Nôtre.

278

278 Austria. Schönbrunn Palace, Vienna, completed in 1750. Façade overlooking the park, 185 yds. long.

280 Russia. St Petersburg (Leningrad). The Neva seen from the Admiralty. In the background, the eastern end of Vasilievsky island, known as Strielka.

279 Peter the Great in armour.

Most rulers needed to do no more than go along with the current tastes of the period to imitate Versailles. For Peter the 279 Great*, however, the building of St Petersburg was a revolutionary step. The Tsar abandoned Moscow and transferred not only his court and the nobility but also business men and labourers alike to his new capital. For some years he even made it an offence to build in stone anywhere else, in order to attract masons to 280 the new city. The *Strielka**, one of the loveliest vistas of St Petersburg, was an island built up out of the waters of the Neva delta in 1703, in spite of a desperate shortage of brick and stone. Within twenty years, forty thousand men had been resettled from all over Russia, giving the nation the vital shipping outlet on to the Baltic without which the country could never develop. The Tsar also brought back from his long tour in Europe a strong desire to westernise the traditional court of Moscow.

To judge by the nationalities of the men summoned by Peter the Great, all Europe seemed to be collaborating to give Russia its new gateway. First he called on the Dutch to open up the port. Then he commissioned de Waal, from Flanders, to build his first residence, the Podzorny Palace. Then came Germans, Italians and Frenchmen to take the entire layout of the city in hand because it had been growing too untidy. Under the direction of the Frenchman Le Blond, a pupil of Le Nôtre, a plan took shape which had in it something of both Versailles and Amsterdam: Amsterdam because of the system of three concentric canals (Morskaia, Moika and Fontanka) draining the marshes of the delta, and Versailles because of the three great avenues, known as 'prospects', converging on the gilded 282 spire of the Admiralty*. The most important of these was the Nevsky Prospect, so called because it touched the Neva at both ends where the river looped between the Admiralty and the monastery of St Alexander Nevsky. 'In this way the

148

St Petersburg.

281 Russia. Petrodvorietz (Peterhof), near Leningrad. Fountains at the Great Palace.

design of St Petersburg clearly reflects the two artistic influences which followed the creation of Peter's Russia: those of Holland and France.'

Like the rest of his contemporaries, Peter the Great succumbed to the charm of Versailles. It was to a team of Frenchmen that he entrusted the creation, on the same inevitable model, of his palace and gardens on the shores of the Gulf of Finland. The German name of his 281 palace, the Peterhof*, was to be turned into the Russian Petrodvorietz, but the small pavilions scattered about the park still keep the French names of Monplaisir, l'Ermitage, and Marly.

This new royal capital, which was also the centre of civil and military administration, needed an influx of commerce and industry if it were to function effectively. At Kronstadt, therefore, on an island blocking the Gulf of Finland, west of St Petersburg, the Tsar established an arsenal and laid the foundations of Russian sea-power.

282 Russia. St Petersburg. The Admiralty on the south bank of the Neva.

The industrial city is ideal—
before the Industrial Revolution puts it to the test.

283 Austria. Benedictine monastery of Melk, situated on a rock overlooking the Danube.

At the close of the Eighteenth Century Europe was more fertile than ever in new ideas, whether philosophical or scientific, and a rich harvest of technical discoveries was promised for the future. But the influence of the past was by no means to be ignored.

As they moved down the Danube in 1805, the soldiers of Napoleon's Grande Armée were astonished at the sight of the huge monastery of Melk*. Its dome, its bell-towers, its pillared façades were typical of the Baroque style which had left such a lasting impression in Italy, Bavaria and elsewhere.

But these great, aristocratic buildings were already beginning to give way to innovations heralding an entirely new era. The building of edifices dedicated to manufacture, which had hitherto been regarded as a form of handicraft, was now assuming a greater importance in its own right. In France both princes and small nobility felt obscurely that their class privileges were threatened and began to own factories in increasing numbers. In Great Britain the industrial revolution was just beginning to get under way.

The architect Ledoux had visions of an idealised industrial plant. He envisaged factories designed on the scale of a town*.

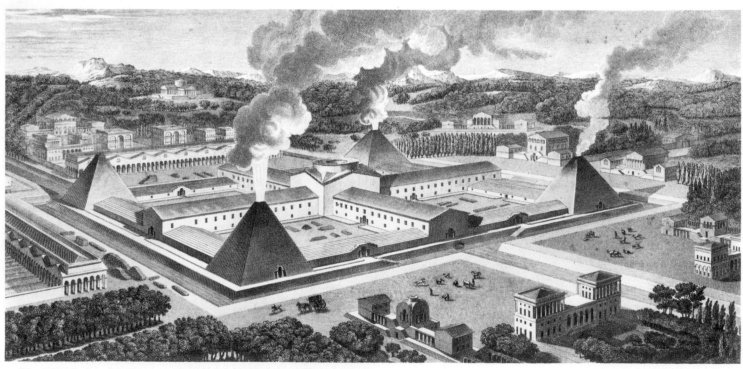

284 The Ideal Industrial City, as envisaged by the French architect Ledoux.

Suez and Manhattan

5

the new
iron age

Columns and obelisks are raised,
as of old, to celebrate the triumphs of princes.

These pictures of the erection of columns and obelisks seem to have strayed from an earlier part of this book, for here we are at the opening of an age which saw the construction of the Suez Canal, Brooklyn Bridge and the Eiffel Tower. We are at the opening of an age which witnessed the spread of democracy through Europe after the French Revolution of 1789 had marked the end of the days when absolute monarchs could command infinite resources to carry out their whims.

In the years between 1789 and 1830 the energy of Europe had been devoted for the most part to the waging of war. Military organisation had reached an unprecedented scale as war was waged on several fronts, and huge fleets patrolled the seas. Boundaries changed, thrones toppled. A new society was emerging, dedicated to individualism, opposed to inherited power. Now individualism has ever been the bane of great public works. Napoleon's grandiose plans for Paris (the Palais de Chaillot) and Rome (the Capitol) never left the drawing-board.

Yet those princes who had succeeded in riding out the storm were quick to confirm their prestige with royal monuments. In 1834 a French architect, Montferrand, supervised the erection of Alexander I's
285 column★ in the square outside the Winter Palace at St Petersburg. It was carved from a single block of rose-coloured granite, brought from Finland, and glorified the leader of the Holy Alliance as 'the Archangel of Russia'.

On October 28th, 1836, two hundred thousand spectators watched with bated breath as the 250-ton obelisk of Rameses II was set up in the Place de la Concorde in Paris. It had been brought from
286 Luxor★ by order of King Louis-Philippe, and several hundred men were needed to lift it from the cradle in which it had travelled and raise it into position by means of an elaborate system of blocks and tackles and pulleys. The raising of these huge monoliths required as much organisation as the building of monuments of even greater size, and constituted in itself a considerable feat of engineering. The positioning of the winches, the relative tensions on different cables at varying stages of the monolith's trajectory, the force of the wind and many other considerations had to be studied in elaborate detail beforehand.

285 Russia. Erection of column in honour of Tsar Alexander, St Petersburg.

286 Egypt. Luxor. Removal of the obelisk of Rameses destined for the Place de la Concorde, Paris.

In England, as engineers look ahead, architects revive the traditions of the past.

The Times of November 29th, 1814, reported in its columns on the rapid development of the steam engine: "A mechanism to which one would be tempted to attribute a life of its own has just been invented. . . . All that is required of those who look after this machine is that they keep it running and control it."

Preserved from the devastation inflicted on the continent of Europe during the Napoleonic wars, England was already drawn into the Industrial Revolution when the Emperor of the French met his final defeat at Waterloo in 1815. The flying shuttle and the spinning jenny were already in use in textile mills and iron-built boats were coming into use on the canals. James Watt's invention of the steam engine had made England the first nation in the world to move into the age of modern technology.

But although industry was breaking new ground, architecture was going back over the old. The Houses of Parliament* at Westminster, burnt down in 1834, were rebuilt in a style which went back to the Middle Ages. With its eleven courtyards, its eleven hundred rooms, its hundred staircases and endless miles of corridors, it was a worthy residence for the House of Lords and the House of Commons. The Victoria Tower, three hundred and thirty feet high, was to be the tallest square tower in the world, though the Big Ben clock tower was to achieve greater renown. Its bell weighs 13½ tons and can be heard five miles away. Pugin, who designed the building in collaboration with Barry, was later to become the chief exponent of the neo-Gothic movement that left its mark on churches and public buildings throughout the country.

England was still largely an agricultural country, made up of great estates in the possession of a landed aristocracy. Up and down the country, manor houses were being built and old ones modernised. New land was being brought under cultivation thanks to improvements made in drainage and irrigation by the use of earthenware pipes. One of the greatest building enterprises of this period was the completion and restoration of Windsor Castle*, which was to be one of Queen Victoria's principal residences.

287 England. Houses of Parliament, Westminster. Façade overlooking the Thames. 315 yds. long.

288 England. Windsor Castle, near London. ➤

A steam-engine mounted on wheels brings far-reaching changes to Europe.

It was in England, too, that an event took place which was to have an unforeseeable effect on the entire world. On September 27th, 1825, the first railway line, connecting the towns of Stockton and Darlington in the north of England, was officially opened and Stephenson's locomotive made its first appearance before an admiring public.

Not even *The Times* could conceal its astonishment:

'Three steam engines, each capable of as much power as fifty horses, pulled thirteen laden waggons up on to the inclined plane which formed the tracks. Here they were harnessed to a mobile machine named the *Experience*, together with a number of other waggons carrying the official party, the guests and the stockholders, thirty-four waggons in all, in one of which musicians were executing gay fanfares. When the signal was given the train set off, to the delighted cheers of the crowd. At the steepest part of the incline the train reached a speed of twenty-six miles per hour.'

Two sentences from the report which appeared in the *Moniteur Universel* serve as an indication of the way in which this new development opened up a whole new world of possibilities: 'On the outskirts of Darlington, the railway runs parallel to the main highway. The train caught up with stage-coaches on the road and passed them rapidly.' The era of mechanised transport had begun.

Building railways, even under ideal conditions, was a difficult and exacting task, demanding minutely accurate advance calculations. If the lines were to run as directly as possible between two given points, extensive works had often to be undertaken to level the land. 289 290 Embankments, cuttings* and tunnels* had to be made, and the vast quantities of earth and rock that were shifted often bore little enough relation to the size of the engines and the trains they pulled. The Tring cutting, for example, on the London to Birmingham line, was four miles long and fifty-six feet deep, and involved the removal of over a million cubic yards of soil. The railways were also responsible for a new era of bridge-building on an unprecedented scale.

By 1842 there were 5,500 miles of railway line in Europe, and 14,000 miles by 1850. Britain kept her lead in railway engineering and soon began to

290 England. Completion of a tunnel on the Coventry line, near Rugby. 1837.

form links with the Continent. The number of lines laid between Paris and the Channel ports indicated the increasing volume of Anglo-French traffic. The line from Paris, via Rouen to Le Havre, was begun by an Irishman in 1840, and many English and an even greater number of Irish workmen crossed the channel to form the nucleus of the gangs who laid these tracks. Iron and other necessary materials were either brought from England or else manufactured in France in factories built by Englishmen.

For perhaps the first time a great undertaking was not an end in itself but was to have a permanent and far-reaching effect on the economy as a whole. In the words of one French historian: 'Railways made it possible to obtain machinery, coal and raw materials at low cost and to deliver the finished product to the coastal ports. They encouraged a flow of workers into the towns and their distribution to places where there was work for them. They also helped to absorb surplus labour from agricultural areas. They gave rise to a more mobile economy. They also hastened the decline of rural life. Wider distribution of goods at lower cost and at greater speed was to make necessities of things which in the Eighteenth Century had been luxuries.'

289 England. A cutting on the Liverpool–Manchester railway.

Growing industries have an insatiable appetite for coal. The green countryside pays the price.

291 France. Mining country showing open shafts and hand-drawn trucks. Engraving by Bonhommé.

The scene of man's great works had shifted from the palaces, fortresses and temples of earlier ages and moved to industry. With the growing importance of steam locomotion came the era of coal 291 and the coal mine. Whole regions* were transformed into a wasteland of pits and slag heaps as the needs of industry made ceaseless demands on the wealth of the mines.

Previously coal had played only an unimportant part in engineering and construction. Wood and iron had been the raw materials for the smelting of iron, but the increased productivity began to lead to serious shortages of wood in the industrial districts of England, Belgium and the Ruhr. From the end of the

Eighteenth Century coal gradually took the place of wood in all the larger foundries, and coal mining assumed an ever-increasing importance. Britain took the lead in exploiting the potentialities of her coal seams, and by 1851 the industry employed some two hundred thousand men. Land bearing seams of coal could make large fortunes for the owners, though the legions of engineers and miners could alter the entire face of the landscape. At Whitehaven, in Cumberland, a whole system of galleries, supported by pillars carved out of the coal itself, ran far into the hills. The shafts were dug and the coal brought out by hand, but it was many years before the invention of the safety lamp gave the

miners any sort of protection against the explosions caused by gases or firedamp. In the Rhine district a type of open-cast mining remained in operation, for this reason, as late as 1850.

The industry progressed rapidly, however, as one new development led to another. By 1820 there were sixty-five steam engines in use in French mines, and by 1830 the number had grown to a hundred and twenty-five. The mechanical drill replaced the pick-axe; pit-props became more reliable, as also did the pumping and ventilation systems and the methods of bringing the coal to the surface; new safety devices were elaborated for the mounting of the cages. Mining engineers dug deeper and deeper

292 A coal-mine in 1883. Spanish engraving showing work at the coal-face, evacuation of the coal, water being pumped, and a cross-section of the mine.

293 France. Pit-pony going down a mine.

292 in search of rich seams, and by 1860 mines had begun to assume the appearance★ which was to alter comparatively little right up the present. Tens of thousands of men—and in those days women and children too—were concentrated in the man-made valleys between the towering slag heaps of the 'black country'. They worked long hours at the coal-face, in unbelievably difficult and dangerous conditions, for pitifully small wages. Although mechanisation made it easier to pump water out of the mines, and to wash and screen the coal, it still had to be mined by hand. Vast 293 numbers of men and ponies★ were needed to dig the shafts, to prop the tunnels, to hew and haul the coal.

Production had to be increased at all costs, but the demand more than kept pace with it. In France production went up more than five times between 1820 and 1847, and still could not keep pace with consumption. In thirty years coal had come into general use in the cities of Europe and was indispensable both to industry and to transport. Coal production over the whole of Europe rose from nine million tons in 1790 to ninety million in 1880.

The industrial prosperity of the Nineteenth Century was essentially based on private enterprise. Individual pit-owners, like the Anglo-Belgian industrialist, Cockerill, also controlled blast furnaces and forges, employing thousands of men.

The new materialism has no care for the landscape.   Production must come first.

294 England. View of Wolverhampton, Staffordshire in 1866. On the edge of the 'Black Country', the iron and steel district.

295 Casting iron in a British naval shipyard, mid-XIXth C.

The French historian Michelet, on a visit to England, was horrified, as were all his contemporaries, by the nightmarish transformation which had come over the towns caught up in the Industrial 294 Revolution, especially in the Midlands★ and the North. Leeds, he said, was 'a veritable hive of humanity, a thick cluster of giant chimneys. The cathedral is smothered by these tall spires, belching their clouds of black smoke into the sky.'

Machines are invented, and machines to make machines. Man is a cog in the wheel.

The effects of the new industrial age on the landscape were the more alarming in that vast tracts of what had hitherto been open countryside were made over to the needs of industry; the new towns and factory suburbs, built in haste, were to remain a permanent feature.

In the Eighteenth Century three generations of the Darby family developed a process for converting coal into coke to feed the ever-hungry blast furnaces. People began to talk of the 'Steel Age'. But the method of 'puddling' or stirring the ore in order to expel the carbon was still a particularly unpleasant task for the workmen engaged in it. It was their job to stir the molten metal and then hammer it, while still hot, for hours at a time. In 1856 Henry Bessemer discovered that the right amount of carbon could be removed by simply pouring the molten ore into a cold receptacle and passing a current of cold air through it. His discovery laid the foundations of the steel industry and of the immense steel fortunes made in such towns as Sheffield, Le Creusot and Essen. The giant Bessemer converters, lined with fire-proof clay, were able to process ten to twenty tons of the molten metal in a few minutes.

In 1830 the Duc d'Orléans had the old wooden fabric of the Palais Royal demolished and replaced by a metal structure. In all countries with sufficient resources metal replaced wood in ship-building. The naval shipyards of England*, France*, Germany and the United States hummed with activity, as rolling mills and hydraulic presses moulded and shaped the sheet steel for the hulls of new battleships*.

The use of machine-tools spread to all industries as new requirements engendered new developments. Woodwork was facilitated by mechanical saws and planes. Machine turning, mechanical drills, screw cutters and saws came into use in metal-working. Huge fortunes were built up by the captains of industry who could draw on a vast pool of underpaid labour in the urban areas. By 1848 factories* had reached an enormous size and were organised with all the discipline of a barracks or monastery. Hundreds, sometimes even thousands of workers were crammed into grim sheds to mind the machines; of the two, man and machine, the former was regarded as the more readily expendable.

296 France, 1862. Forging with the aid of a power hammer.

297 Workmen moving armour plating in a naval shipyard.

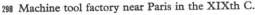

298 Machine tool factory near Paris in the XIXth C.

159

**Confidence in the new technology is boundless.
What once was only planned is now accomplished.**

299

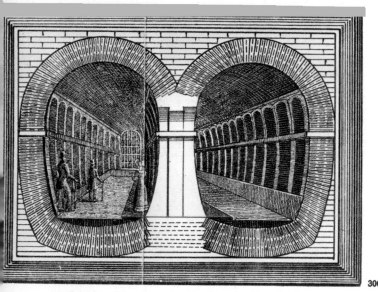

300

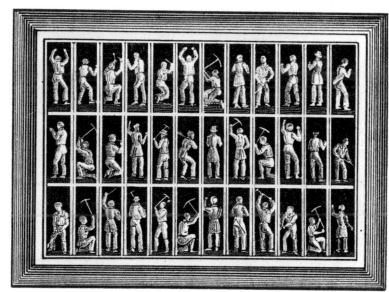

301

299 London. Tunnel under the Thames. Longitudinal section.　300 Caisson used in boring the tunnel.　301 Framework used in tunnelling.

In 1825, the same year as the first railway was opened, another enterprise was begun in England which seemed at the time to verge on insanity. The idea of linking the two banks of the Thames by a tunnel in the eastern district of London had been mooted for almost a century, because the movement of shipping in the busy port of London made the building of another bridge in this sector appear out of the question. The first tunnel project was suggested and discarded as early as 1798. It was followed by others and there were even attempts to put the idea into practice, but these were quickly abandoned under the combined pressure of practical difficulties and public opposition. The idea of attempting to travel underneath the river provoked an almost superstitious fear in the popular mind.

At last an engineer appeared on the scene who embodied all that was boldest and most adventurous in the spirit of the age. Marc-Isambard Brunel was a French-man by birth, a naturalised American, and, at the time of his death, the possessor of an English knighthood. His tunnel* under the Thames was begun on February 16th, 1825, and not opened to the public until February 1843, after eighteen years of continual setbacks. Brunel's idea was to construct thick shafts of brick*, sixty-five feet wide, the first of which was sunk some fifty yards from the bank. By means of these it was possible to dig winding-shafts and then proceed to cutting the actual tunnel underneath the river bed. Brunel personally supervised work in the shafts which was carried out with the help of shields, platforms and derricks*.

Water was continually leaking into the tunnel; the men working on it took fright and there were a number of strikes; twice the tunnel was flooded and the work had to be begun all over again. Brunel did not give up. The London public, sceptical at first, became excited about the project. A writer in one news-paper hailed it lyrically as 'the wonder of all civilised Europe. . . .' Finally the tunnel was completed, the prototype of all the great tunnels built during the Nineteenth Century and the ancestor of the underground railway.

In the years between 1810 and 1850 England was well in the vanguard of the technological progress that was to alter the face of Europe. But not only Europe was on the move. On the other side of the Atlantic the American continent was in a ferment of expansion. In forty years its population had grown from four to twelve million. 'We are still growing', wrote one American in 1817, 'at a great, I might almost say a terrible rate.' Over the half century which followed, the wave of emigrants was to continue, surging ever westwards by easy stages. Thousands of covered wagons streamed to the west whenever an economic or political crisis brought a recession in the

302 U.S.A. Oklahoma. Pioneers bound for the west. From the film *Cimarron*.

eastern states, and the young families who went to start life afresh in the virgin lands beyond the Ohio were to found some of the greatest industrial cities of the Twentieth Century. The first stage of their journey was to Pittsburgh, where they stopped for fresh supplies. There they could get a boat, at a cost of sixty cents (5/-) per ton, and sail down the Ohio River which flows westward into the Mississippi. From here the pioneers would take to their covered wagons again for the long trek, braving the Indians and the desert, to push back the frontiers that marked the westernmost point to which the human tide had penetrated. The last stage of the journey would end in a mad gallop as the pioneers rushed to stake their claims on a plot of ground in one more
302 new state *

At first the inhabitants of these new western states were either cattlemen or farmers. The grasslands were given over to cattle- and sheep-raising while more

and more land was brought under cultivation. Then one day in 1847 a wheelwright named Marshall happened to pick up a few pieces of yellow metal in the region of Sacramento, in the same month that the United States acquired California from Mexico, and started the gold rush. From 1849 onwards twenty thousand men fought their way across desert plains and over the Rocky Mountains, in the face of constant attacks by the Indians, to the peaks of the Sierra Nevada. They left a fifth of their number on the road. Another twenty thousand came from Asia. In all more than three
303 hundred thousand gold prospectors * rushed to make their fortunes in the new Eldorado, crowding into ramshackle hovels, building shanty towns that died as suddenly as they grew up, and often gaining nothing for their pains. Many prospectors abandoned their search to settle down as farmers in the fertile agricultural valleys of California.

303 Californians panning gold. 1850.

Early New York
is a city of spires.

The expansion and development of the Far West did nothing to lessen America's dependence on the 'old' States of New England. Pittsburg remained the gateway to the west and Baltimore the pivot of its industrial productivity. The railway was not extended as far as Chicago or St Louis until 1850. The most important part of America was still the Atlantic coast, and over the cities of the Atlantic coast New York reigned supreme.

At this time New York meant Man-304 hattan Island*, which the Dutch had bought from the Indians a hundred years earlier for twenty-five guilders' worth of glass beads. There was as yet no indication of today's skyscrapers and no bridges connected the island to the mainland, but the city was already beginning to feel cramped between its three rivers— the Hudson, the East and the Harlem. From an early stage New York was laid out on a geometrical plan, divided up by straight avenues. Fifth Avenue, Wall Street and Broadway had already received their names.

New York was the first great city of the machine age and it increased in size with unprecedented speed, as new suburbs sprang up almost overnight. Trucks and mechanical cranes were imported from England, as well as an impressive number of new prefabricated building materials. Moreover, for the first time doors, window-frames and various other components were being turned out off an assembly line. At the same time dock installations were extending up the river banks and round the estuary until New York harbour was to become the largest port in the world.

Only one city was so far in a position to rival New York. This was much further inland on the shores of the Great Lakes. In 1832 a hundred or so pioneers had built their log cabins on the marshy soil of Chicago. Its position as a lake port and major railway junction made it an essential link for traffic going north, south, east or west, and it rapidly assumed the position of economic capital of the Federation. When its eight square miles of wooden houses burned down in the disastrous fire of 1871 immigrants from all over the world rebuilt the town in brick and stone and laid out acres of parkland stretching for over fifteen miles along the shores of Lake Michigan.

304 New York. Manhattan Island about 1865.

The railways move westward across America,
drawing the surplus population of the eastern states.

305 U.S.A. Crossing the frozen Missouri by rail in 1857.

306 U.S.A. Salt Lake City, Utah, founded by the Mormons in 1847.

The railway link between New York and Philadelphia was such a valuable investment that a number of companies were working on the project at the same time. From 1830 onwards stretches of line were also built, more or less at random, linking Philadelphia with Washington, Baltimore with the Ohio and Mississippi valleys. Nobody at the time was much worried by the fact that the twenty-thousand miles of existing track had been built under the auspices of a large number of rival companies each one using a different gauge. Rail travel was the rage and superseded all other forms of transport. Tracks were laid to the virgin lands, even temporarily across frozen rivers*, and the pioneers would clamber aboard bound for 'the end of the line'. The Federal Government somewhat rashly accorded to the railway companies a tract of land twenty miles wide along the entire route of the tracks.

At the same time the Mormon prophet Brigham Young led his band of a hundred and forty-two men, three women and two children to the entrance of a blazing, desert valley, bounded at the far end by a salt lake, and gravely announced: 'This is the place.'*

His determination, a blend of excessive mysticism and extremely practical economic sense, was to bear fruit in the town of Salt Lake City. Young's pioneers organised the first planned system of irrigation in the United States and made Utah a fertile region. It is still largely in the hands of the Mormons to this day.

A thriving coastal trade had grown up between New York and other Atlantic cities* which was succeeded by some rivalry in attracting European trade. The first American shipyards launched the great sailing ships known as 'clippers'. Six or eight times as long as their width, these splendid ships were built for speed: they carried from three to five masts, up to two hundred feet high, and a magnificent spread of canvas. With a favourable wind they could cross the Atlantic in eleven days. The steamboats with their paddle-wheels looked clumsy beside them, but before long the screw propeller was to give the steamships their lead in the Atlantic trade.

The early American industrialists were setting up their factories* in broad, open sites where their raw materials could be transported either by rail or by canal.

307 New York. Docks handling traffic with Boston and Baltimore in 1869. Sail- and steam-boats, and grain elevators are shown.

308 U.S.A. Factory in 1876. The buildings cover a wide area and have direct access to rail and canal transport.

The Crystal Palace is built out of
metal and glass, a foretaste of architecture to come.

309 London. The Great Exhibition, 1851. Crystal Palace, made entirely of metal and glass.

The use of a cast-iron framework for buildings was becoming increasingly popular with architects. New railway stations, market arcades and shops tended to have metal frameworks, and such buildings as St Isaac in St Petersburg, the library of St Geneviève in Paris and the enormous hot-houses at Chatsworth in England and at Kiev in Russia proved the utility of this material. But its most spectacular use was undoubtedly in the 309 Crystal Palace* built for the Great Exhibition of 1851 and admired by visitors from all over the world. Newspapers published the statistics of the building, which was set up in Hyde Park for the Exhibition and later moved to a permanent site. It was 1,608 feet long and 104 feet high. 3,300 cast-iron pillars made up the framework, which was entirely filled in with glass. 2,224 cast-iron girders carried the weight of the galleries in the 310 main body of the building*. The twenty-four acres of glass which covered its surface weighed four hundred and twenty tons.

The architect, Sir Joseph Paxton, was a distinguished gardener and horti-culturist well used to working with iron and glasswork. For the Crystal Palace, which he designed almost at the last moment and which was adopted in face of competition from two hundred and forty-five other schemes, he used a similar plan to that which he had used for the Chatsworth conservatories. A re-

310 Central Exhibition Hall at the Crystal Palace. 108 ft. high, 615 yds. long. Original photo.

Where the small tradesman exposed his wares the spacious department store now caters for all needs.

311 France. Paris. The 'Printemps' department store, in 1885. Four sales floors, a restaurant and basement for stores and machinery.

markably resourceful man, he grappled with every problem as it occurred and overcame each separate difficulty of execution just as he had overcome the problems of the grand design. All that could be done by mechanical means was done. To build the Crystal Palace in the short space of five months materials had to be ordered and deliveries made in the swiftest possible time, and each component part had to be made to fit as accurately as possible into place to avoid delays on the site. It was a gigantic task of organisation and timing.

A few years later a small French businessman named Aristide Boucicaut had the idea of a permanent exhibition of all the latest novelties and fashions with a special appeal to women. The immediate success of his *Bon Marché* led to the rise of the department store. The opening of the *Louvre* department store coincided with the Universal Exhibition of 1855, and the architect of the *Printemps*★ took advantage of the current vogue for glass and ironwork to make the most of it in designing the building. At the same time new stores on similar lines were opening in many of the larger cities such as London (Harrods and Selfridges), Berlin, New York and even as far afield as Moscow★.

311

312

312 Russia. Outside a big Moscow store, late XIXth C.

Once the city gates have been thrown open the ramparts must be torn down.

313 London, 1851. Gang of workmen resurfacing the Strand, directed by top-hatted foreman with a baton.

The cities of Europe were changing rapidly under the pressures of the new railways, factories and increasing urban populations. Such innovations as paving with wooden blocks, tarmacadam surfaces and gas lighting kept a whole army of workmen permanently occupied and altered the look of city streets. Any street was liable to become a building site almost overnight. In London old bridges were modernised, new bridges built, parks and gardens laid out, while railway stations, markets, government buildings, offices, clubs, churches and schools sprouted from one end of town to the other—monuments to the prosperity of Victorian England. The Strand* was resurfaced completely in the year of the Great Exhibition.

313

Rotterdam, at the mouth of the Rhine, demolished much of its medieval quarter* in order to take advantage of

314

Germany's new commercial and industrial prosperity. The Nieuwe Waterweg, a channel excavated at this time, was navigable by ships of the very largest tonnage at all times and in all weathers and ensured a direct communication between Rotterdam and the sea.

During the long reign of the Emperor Franz-Josef (1848–1916), the city of Vienna underwent a complete transformation. In 1857 work was begun on the demolition of the old city walls, which were replaced by a broad avenue, known as the Ring. Here were situated the new Opera House, the Parliament building, the City Hall and other monumental new edifices. Two long aqueducts brought fresh water to the city from the Alps. In the same way many other cities were ridding themselves of their belts of medieval fortifications.

More than any other city, Paris was

rapidly assuming a new face. With Napoleon III there came to the fore a generation of brilliant technicians, steeped in the ideas which Saint-Simon had expounded half a century earlier. They were determined to create a new order to replace the one the Revolution had overthrown in 1789. One of the means by which they hoped to achieve this was by organised city planning.

Saint-Simon had remarked that the new prince of modern times was the engineer. Now those of his followers engaged in industry, finance and public works were putting forward a wide assortment of ambitious projects. Many of them were wildly impracticable but among them were a few that have since been realised, such as a European railway network and the cutting of the Suez canal. They did all they could to transform Paris, which in 1850 stood in

**A more spacious age requires more spacious streets;
the modern thoroughfare must be broad and uncluttered.**

314 Holland. Laying the 'Birnnen Rote' through old Rotterdam.

considerable need of improvements. There were insufficient schools, cemeteries, railway-stations, open spaces, fountains and covered markets, and the streets had not been resurfaced since before the Revolution. Among the new amenities were the great covered market, called
315 Les Halles*, extensive parks, such as the Bois de Boulogne, the Bois de Vincennes and the Buttes-Chaumont, broad streets and, most necessary of all, sewers. Big cities were slow to learn how to organise adequate arrangements for refuse disposal, even in the Nineteenth Century. An engineer named Belgrand was appointed 'grand master of subterranean Paris'. He designed a vast system of primary and subsidiary sewers to drain the city's waste away to the lower reaches of the Seine or to carry it through miles of pipe-lines to fertilise farm lands far away from the city.

315 France. Les Halles, Paris, after completion in 1860.

Britain launches the 'Leviathan' but, for all its size, it disappoints expectations.

316 England. Hull of the *Leviathan*, the future *Great Eastern*, before installation of masts and funnels.

317 Winding transatlantic cables in one of the *Great Eastern*'s holds.

318 The *Great Eastern* laying the transatlantic cable.

The Atlantic Cable puts the
New World within talking distance of the Old.

The eighteen-sixties were to witness the inauguration of three of the most ambitious projects ever undertaken, and among the first of practical universal significance. The first of them, in chronological order, was the laying of the first transatlantic cable between Europe and America, and it was followed by the building of the American transcontinental railway and the cutting of the Suez canal.

A little earlier than this, an enterprise of a different nature had fallen short of expectations because it was ahead of its time: the construction of the largest passenger steamer in the world. The 316 *Leviathan*★ was designed by the same Brunel who had bored the first tunnel under the Thames (see page 160) and was built at Liverpool. She embodied many new departures in shipbuilding: she was constructed entirely of steel, displaced twenty-three thousand tons, and was driven by a screw propeller twenty-three feet high in addition to her paddle-wheels fifty-five feet in diameter. The *Leviathan* made her first Atlantic crossing in 1860 and the following year carried the largest cargo in the history of navigation, five thousand tons of wheat. But her builders went bankrupt, the boilers exploded, the vessel ran aground: she never won the public favour and her three thousand berths never filled up.

However, a new use was found to save the *Leviathan* from complete disgrace. Many countries already possessed telegraph cables strung from poles, and in 1851 the invention of an adequate insulation had made it possible to run a cable across the English Channel from Dover to Calais. A far-sighted American industrialist named Cyrus Field conceived the idea of creating a similar link between Europe and America. Despite a good deal of opposition from sceptical businessmen, he obtained the co-operation of the British and American governments and set up his Atlantic Cable Company which he succeeded in floating within a month. After this, though, everything started to go wrong. The first cable, two thousand five hundred miles long, between Ireland and Newfoundland was so heavy that it had to be laid in two sections, joined in the middle of the Atlantic by two ships, the *Agamemnon* and the *Niagara*. As if determined to cause trouble, the cable snapped twice, broke loose during a storm, shattering everything on the ship's deck,

319 Cross-section of steamer designed in 1890 by Bessemer to overcome effects of rolling.

and made it necessary to call off the work four times before finally, on August 18th, 1858, the first telegram was sent from Europe to America. Its message was: 'Glory to God in the highest and on earth peace to men of goodwill.' The cable had been in use for only a short while before it rusted through and snapped again, and work had to begin again from the beginning. But by this time America was in the throes of the Civil War and the cable had to wait for another six years. When Cyrus Field finally succeeded in manufacturing a new cable, three thousand miles long and weighing five thousand tons, it was discovered that only one ship existed capable of carrying such a load: the *Leviathan*. She was rechristened the *Great Eastern* and given a chance to redeem herself from disgrace. A complete refit was necessary in order to accommodate the three cable-drums resting on a 317 concrete bed★.

The first crossing was plagued by disaster. There were attempts at sabotage

instigated by transatlantic steamship companies who saw their livelihood threatened by the new cable; the cable ended by snapping and sank in two thousand fathoms of water. Undaunted, Cyrus Field decided to fish it up. He launched a new subscription, canvassed for public support and had a new cable made, this time covered with a new kind of insulating tape invented not long before by Chatterton. Lastly he had further modifications made to the *Great* 318 *Eastern*★. On July 27th, 1866, the now indestructible cable was unrolled into the sea off the coast of Ireland, to re-emerge on the other side of the Atlantic at Newfoundland. The *Great Eastern* had saved her reputation but her enormous size destined her to an early retirement. However, her fate did not deter others from trying to devise more comfortable means of making the crossing between Europe and America. Some of their solutions 319 were quaint★, but their efforts paved the way for the luxury liners of today.

320 U.S.A. Transcontinental railway, 1866. The engine is equipped with a cow-catcher.

320 The American transcontinental railroad* owed its origin in part to the pressure of European immigration to the eastern states, in part to the lure of the western territories. Until the railways came the only way to cross the continent of America had been by covered wagon or by water. One of the most important waterways was the canal from New York to Lake Erie which had carried thirteen thousand vessels by 1830. In 1862 President Lincoln set the final seal on the project when he signed the Pacific Railroad Act, authorising the construction of eighteen hundred miles of track to connect Omaha with San Francisco through the Rockies and the Sierra Nevada. Omaha was already linked with New York through Chicago.

The president's decision resulted in fierce competition between the two companies authorised to undertake the construction of the new railroad. The Central Pacific Railroad (C.P.R.) started from the Pacific end of the line and was intended to join up with the Union Pacific Railroad (U.P.R.) working from Omaha. Each mile of track the companies laid increased their profits, making it in the interests of each of them to extend their own line as far as possible into their rival's territory. The tension between the two competing companies mounted to fever pitch. The U.P.R., working westwards, had to lay their track through country where the Indians were sometimes friendly* but more often fiercely hostile. Their supply of wood for the sleepers all came from the thick poplar groves along the banks of the Missouri. Frequently the track-layers did not wait for the completion of a tunnel, but continued their work beyond the point at which it was calculated to emerge, leaving behind them small, isolated gangs to finish the lengths of line still under con-

321

struction. As the railhead moved westward so did a complete mobile township, with its own church, bank, offices and inevitable saloons, which served the needs of the railway engineers and labourers.

As the C.P.R. started from the Pacific coast, all its steel for the tracks and rolling stock had to be brought by the long and dangerous sea-journey round Cape Horn. There was a complete lack of steel and coal in California and a dire shortage of manpower. The hordes of gold prospectors in the country were reluctant to sign on. As a last resort the company recruited Chinese immigrants in their thousands. There were eventually seventeen thousand men working on the lines as they gradually drew closer together; the working conditions were as often as not subhuman. The track-layers pushed ahead without stopping to wait for the bridge-builders and tunnel-builders to finish their

To travel in comfort
is a novel idea, introduced by Pullman.

321 U.S.A. Building the transcontinental railway.

work, and all the while a fleet of vessels ferried materials round Cape Horn and up the Pacific coast. At last, when the meeting seemed inevitable, the two lines seemed to become oblivious of each other and pushed stolidly forward past each other, running parallel for two hundred miles, as neither company would concede victory to the other. Finally the Government had to intervene and the two ends of the line were joined, with four rivets made of precious metals, on May 10th, 1869, seven years ahead of schedule. Pullman's 322 luxurious sleeping-cars * could now run from coast to coast.

In these early sleepers the beds were curtained off down one side of the car, which was still lighted by lamps and candles. Heating was supplied by a stove at each end of the carriage. Printed on the tickets issued for these 'hotel-cars' was a request that passengers remove their boots before getting into bed.

322 U.S.A. The first sleeping car, put into operation on the New York Central Railroad in 1860.

173

The sea route to the Orient
lies through the deserts of Egypt—the Suez Canal is built.

323 Egypt. Camels hauling the parts of a dredger to be used in building the Suez canal.

324 Construction workers beside the canal at Ismailia during the last few days' work.

325 Bust of the giant statue of Ferdinand de Lesseps on arrival at Port Said.

In the years 1869–1870, when for the first time men could travel by rail from the Atlantic to the Pacific and by boat across the isthmus of Suez from the Mediterranean to the Indian Ocean, the world seemed to shrink to half its size.

A Frenchman, Ferdinand de Lesseps, founded a society in 1846 to study the possibilities of cutting a canal through the Isthmus of Suez. He succeeded in interesting Napoleon III in the project and in winning over a number of French business men who were imbued with the principles of Saint-Simon. It was Lesseps, too, who succeeded in obtaining not only the permission but the active co-operation of the Khedive Ismail Pasha, and in persuading him that the difference in the level of the sea at either end of the proposed canal, a factor which had discouraged all the earlier attempts, was nearer ten inches than ten yards as had previously been supposed. His enthusiasm inspired the entire undertaking and in ten years his determination never faltered.

Work began on the site on April 15th, 1859, and at first the methods employed were no less rudimentary than those in use thousands of years before in the times of the Pharaohs and of the Persian king Darius who had also dug canals through the isthmus, though these did not, in fact, connect the two seas but simply formed a link between the Red Sea and the Nile. Thirty thousand *fellagha*, recruited on the spot, dug out the canal bed with picks and shovels and carried away the soil in baskets, just as they had in Ancient Egypt. The climate, exhaustion, cholera and the pace of work imposed by the

326 Port Said Roads. Photo taken the day the canal was opened, November 17th, 1869, with ships flying the flags of all nations.

overseers took their toll. In spite of the eleven medical centres under the supervision of seventeen doctors, more than six thousand died, including six of the doctors. Food, shelter and supplies had to be laid on in a barren desert where there was not so much as a drop of water. Machinery was brought from Europe and carried over the desert by camel cara-
323 vans *; what had been empty desert became a swarming community as technicians of all nationalities arrived to lend
324 their assistance in the enterprise *. By the end of 1865 the equipment assembled between Port Said and Suez included fifty powerful dredgers, complete with

pumps, twenty steam cranes, a hundred and twenty-nine lighters, thirty mechanical hoists and twenty locomotives. Work continued at a furious rate. In 1867 de Lesseps formally christened the new city founded on Lake Timsah Ismailia, after the reigning sheikh.

By October 1869, when the immense task was almost completed, and shallow-draft ships could already sail through the canal, the total volume of earth dug or dredged out of the canal-bed had reached seventy-four million cubic metres.
325 De Lesseps deserved the colossal statue * which was erected to him at the entrance to the canal, and which remained on

its pedestal until its removal in 1956.

The formal opening of the Suez Canal on November 17th, 1869, was attended by an impressive gathering of royalty and statesmen. Nearly a hundred ships lay
326 at anchor in Port Said harbour * and at dawn they began to file through the canal. At the head of the convoy was the Empress Eugénie in her two thousand ton yacht *l'Aigle*. She was followed by the Khedive, the Emperor of Austria, innumerable sheiks, pashas, princes from both East and West, millionaires from America and a whole flotilla of ships of all nations. The canal shortened the sea route to the Indies by two-thirds.

Cape Town loses traffic to Port Said.

327 Egypt. Port Said, at the northern or Mediterranean end of the canal. In the background: Lake Menzaleh and sea approach. On right: Port Fuad.

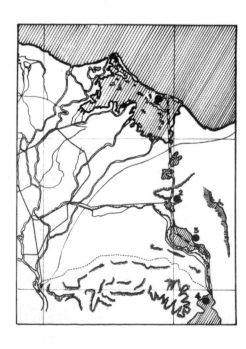

328 Map of the Suez Canal. 1. Port Said. 2. Ismailia. 3. Bitter Lakes. 4. Suez.

327 The construction of the great jetties at the entrance to the Suez canal* presented its own special problems which were solved by a method well in advance of its time. Each jetty is well over fifteen hundred yards long and built to afford protection to the largest ocean-going vessels. Rather than bring from a considerable distance the enormous granite blocks heavy enough to resist the pressure of the waves, the decision was made to manufacture them on the spot. A kind of cement was obtained from the addition of lime to sand dredged from Lake Menzaleh. This mixture was poured into moulds measuring twenty cubic yards and allowed to dry for two months in the parching Egyptian sun. The resulting blocks were as hard as granite and dozens of them were sunk into place each day.

Once past these jetties, ships heading south towards the Red Sea enter the canal, leaving Port Said, with its lighthouse and its complex of docks and harbour installations, to starboard. About forty ships a day can go through the 328 canal*, assembled into convoys which can pass one another at a half-way point specially widened for the purpose. An interval of from two to four thousand yards is allowed between each ship: the margin of safety varies from ship to ship, tankers requiring a greater margin than freighters or passenger ships.

After 1870 Cape Town lost to Suez a considerable part of its ocean-going traffic. Ten years later, however, South Africa hit on a new source of prosperity. A chance event led to what is today one of the most profitable industries in the world.

In 1866 a Boer farmer showed an ostrich hunter a sparkling stone which his children had picked up in a nearby ravine. The ostrich hunter showed the stone to a mineralogist who recognised it for a diamond—twenty-one carats when cut. The news spread and in spite of almost insurmountable natural obstacles, thousands of people flocked to the area to seek their fortunes. At first they were content simply to pan the rivers round about, but then the subsoil of the plateau of Kimberley was found to hold far

But the diamonds of Kimberley create many a fortune in South Africa.

richer deposits. A horde of would-be miners descended on the broad stretch of land between Pretoria and Jagersfontein. To impose some sort of order on the ensuing chaos, Cecil Rhodes combined the numerous, individual stakes all into one large company in 1888. Thus the De Beers organisation was founded to exploit the diamond fields systematically.

The diamonds, formed long ago by sudden, volcanic convulsions taking place below the earth's crust, were mined in near-vertical 'pipes' or 'chimneys' open to the sky, with the help of pulleys. In order to prevent the falls of rock which claimed hundreds of victims in the early days, great quantities of useless rubble had to be removed before the actual mining could begin. As a result the mines, sometimes in the shape of trenches but more often like circular funnels, reached vast proportions. At the Kimberley mine the outermost ring of the funnel is practically a mile round; the Premier mine has a surface area of over seventy-five acres on its deepest level, and is said to be the largest man-made cavity in the world. There are fifteen chimneys on the Kimberley plateau, of which the most 329 important is the Big Hole*. This is nearly four thousand feet deep and produced seventy-five million pounds worth of diamonds between 1871 and 1914. Sixty-five stones weighing over three hundred carats uncut have come from the South African mines. The most famous of these are the Star of the South (125 carats), the Tiffany (128 carats) and, most magnificent of them all, the Cullinan Diamond, which was found in 1905 and weighed 3,106 carats uncut. Diamonds have also been found in other parts of Africa, often on the slopes of valleys, as 330 in Kasai and Katanga* where the seams continue into Angola, and in Sierra Leone. The prospectors' eager and untiring search for diamonds was also a powerful incentive in the development of other mining interests, such as gold, copper and rare metals, in Central and South Africa, and especially in Kasai and Katanga.

It has been estimated that three tons of ore are needed to produce one carat's weight of diamonds in small stones and for a single stone of one carat, two hundred and fifty tons of earth, stones and rock must be blasted, excavated, crushed, washed and sorted.

329 South Africa. Open-cast diamond mining, Kimberley.

330 Congo. Kolwezei Mine, Katanga.

The functional, the productive absorbs
the energy of Europe. Art must be content to copy, to restore.

331 France. Château de Pierrefonds, Oise, fallen into ruins after 1617.

Not all the great works of the Nineteenth Century were strictly utilitarian, nor were they all carried out by financial and industrial concerns using factory labour. Here and there in Europe building works were in progress which had no other end but to satisfy their architects' addiction to bygone days. The architect Viollet-le-Duc, out of sympathy with the fashions of his day, obtained support from Napoleon III and, eventually, authority to restore a number of great Medieval buildings which had fallen to ruin; among these were the Château de Pierrefonds**, the monastery of Vézelay and the ramparts of the city of Carcassone, with their forty-eight towers.

King Ludwig II of Bavaria fell so strongly under the influence of the Wagnerian operas that he commissioned a theatrical designer to build him a fairytale castle* on a mountain spur. Delighted with the result, he wrote to Wagner: 'The situation is the most beautiful that can possibly be imagined. It is isolated and inviolable.'

332 *Ibid.* In course of restoration (1857–1878) by Viollet-le-Duc for the Emperor Napoleon III.

333 Germany. Castle of Neuschwanstein, Bavaria. ▶

Churches remain unfinished.
Factories must take priority.

Following in the footsteps of Viollet-le-Duc, the German Kaiser Wilhelm II completed Cologne Cathedral, which had remained unfinished for several centuries, restored the ramparts of Nuremberg and the cathedral of Metz and restored the castle of Koenigsberg. Cities all over Europe broke out in sudden manifestations of architectural frivolity as though to compensate for an era of strictly utilitarian building. The resulting structures could seldom be described as beautiful, but they made up in opulence and ambitiousness for what they lacked in elegance. In Paris, the new Opera House was opened in 1875, and marble from every quarry in the country had gone into its construction. The Sacré Cœur on Montmartre, built in 1876, involved the sinking of twenty-three shafts a hundred and twenty feet deep. 334 For the great exhibition of 1878* a palace was erected on the hills of the Trocadéro.

Besides Haussmann, one of the greatest influences in the transformation of Paris was the architect Davioud. Landscape artist, hydraulic engineer, theatrical designer, he was ideally suited to the task of designing the Trocadéro. With the help of the engineer Bourdais, he devised 'a verdant hill, a water tower and a concert hall'. In accordance with fashionable taste he included in his design replicas of famous buildings from all over the world: a minaret from Seville Cathedral, moorish arcades from Spain, squat, Romanesque columns, patterns of stone in alternating colours from the churches of Auvergne, artificial grottoes such as were to be found in Italian gardens.

Another great lover of coloured and polished surfaces was the Catalan, Antonio Gaudi y Cornet. More original and more inspired than Davioud, but in the same eclectic tradition, he devoted himself to a task which he knew he would have to leave unfinished, because, he said, a single human existence was not enough time in which to complete it. Another reason doubtless was that the sculptural character of his building and the materials he used made the cost astronomical. The 335 church of the Sagrada Familia* in Barcelona was intended to have twelve spires in honour of the twelve apostles. Only four of them were ever completed. Today the astonishing building still stands as a forlorn witness to one man's vision and determination.

335 Spain. Barcelona. Church of the Sagrada Familia, conceived by Gaudi in 1884 and never completed.

334 Paris. The Trocadéro palace in 1878. Wallpaper design.

181

The Alps no longer divide.

The railways pass through the highest mountain barriers.

336 France. Mont Cenis tunnel from Modane to Bardonecchia. Celebrations on laying the last stone, August 18th, 1871.

337 Mont Cenis. Boring machine; eight power drills prepare the way for blasting.

338 The first locomotive arriving at Modane.

Mont Cenis, Saint Gothard, Simplon:
the watershed is pierced through and through.

339 Austria. Drilling machine, with four steel-tipped drills, used in cutting the Arlberg tunnel.

340 Rotary drill tipped with black diamonds.

On August 18th, 1871, an event took place which marked the happy ending of a project initiated against enormous odds fourteen years before. This was the official opening of the Mont Cenis 336 tunnel*. The tunnel, seven and a half miles long, linked Modane and Bardonecchia through a five-thousand foot mountain.

Work on the tunnel was begun in 1857, with the aid of the old-fashioned pick and shovel, and the rate of progress had been no more than forty yards a month. With the advent of the pneumatic 337 drilling machine* armed with eight long percussion bores the work speeded up. From 1863 onwards the distance separating the two opposite shafts of the tunnel was rapidly reduced until in January 1870 the wall of rock four yards thick, which still divided the French from Italian side, fell at last. The way was clear for the first train to pass underneath 338 the Alps*. Beside the fortune it cost to build, the Mont Cenis tunnel cost the

lives of forty men as a result of rock falls and accidental explosions during the blasting. The completion of the Mont Cenis tunnel encouraged keen competition between French, German, Italian and Swiss companies to build further tunnels; they bored their way through the Alps at numerous different points, often with dangerously inadequate safety precautions.

Several hundred men died in the course of the piercing of the Saint Gothard tunnel in 1880, most of them from the effects of the cold and damp in which they worked. Methods were nevertheless being perfected to speed the work. In the 339 Arlberg tunnel* the Austrians were working with a new rotary drill, armed with a steel bit. The Simplon tunnel was built between 1898 and 1905 to provide a second link between Switzerland and Northern Italy. Here, in order to break through a layer of unexpectedly hard mica-schist that burst like a shell under the normal rotary drills, the engineers

hit on the idea of arming the tips of the 340 drills with black diamonds*. The Simplon Campaign, as it came to be called, was the most dramatic story in all this period of tunnel building. Unprecedented obstacles had to be overcome during its construction. The temperature at the rock-face rose to 130°F. in spite of a power ventilation system. Additional currents of cold air had to be pumped into the tunnel through crates full of ice. Hot water seeped in and deluged the tunnel on the Swiss side and several times work had to be abandoned while the entire tunnel was sealed off with heavy iron gates. As a last resort it was necessary to cut twin tunnels, twenty yards apart, in order to draw off the floodwater from the Italian side.

Substantial advances in the manufacture of explosives, essential for blasting, were made during the construction of these tunnels. Alfred Nobel invented dynamite, a powerful explosive which was fairly safe to handle. In 1880 he patented collodion, used for the St Gothard.

Beside the ancient capital
of the Moguls the British raj builds New Delhi.

341 India. Loading railway engine parts on to elephants. Himalayan frontier, 1885.

By the end of the Nineteenth Century the nations of Europe were extending their power and influence over the whole world and taking with them their grandiose engineering schemes. Cecil Rhodes went all out to build the longest railway in the world, from Capetown to Cairo. In 1934 the French finally opened their railway from the coast into the Congo, after its construction had cost the lives of those who worked on it at the rate of 'one White for every rail and one Negro for every sleeper'. The Germans were projecting a railway running from Berlin to the Persian Gulf via Baghdad. A railway crossed the Andes from Chile to Argentina in South America. The trans-Caspian railway, begun in 1850, travelled across the desert steppes of Central Asia, proceeding from one oasis to the next until it finally emerged, eight years later, at Samarkand. The trans-Siberian railway was begun in 1891, reached Vladivostock in 1902 and Port Arthur in

342 India. Panoramic view of Delhi, former residence of the Great Mogul, with New Delhi, seat of the British administration, built next to it.

343 Australia. Part of the layout of Melbourne, capital of Victoria, in 1890. In the foreground, the docks, showing floating cranes, bridges and railway.

1903. After thousands of years the traditional spice routes were abandoned. The British were among the most enterprising of all in the field of railway and sea communications. In India they laid 341 tracks right up into the Himalayas★. They were energetic builders of naval bases and passenger harbours at key points round the globe, and especially on the route to India.

Technical advances assisted this spread of European influence. From the days of the Egyptian pyramids building materials had scarcely evolved at all. Indeed, some of the secrets known to past builders had been lost. During the construction of the first Eddystone lighthouse an engineer named Smeaton had discovered a form of lime which was known as 'hydraulic' because it hardened under water.

In 1796 James Parker obtained a royal patent for a product which set much more quickly. Then a Yorkshire brickmaker, Joseph Aspdin, discovered a slow-setting cement which he called Portland Cement. To peoples accustomed to building with much rougher or much more splendid materials, be it mud and wattle or marble, Europe brought a new material which permitted faster and often more durable building.

Characteristically the British in India adopted traditional Indian styles for much of their building. This absorption of local atmosphere was most evident in cities like Calcutta, Bombay, whose Malabar Hill was 'the seat of power, wealth and elegance', and New Delhi, a new capital built beside the old one of the Mogul emperors. In New Delhi all the administrative buildings were grouped inside 342 the Imperial Durbar★.

343 The city of Melbourne, in Australia★, was growing rapidly and by 1890 its streets and well-equipped dockyards were considerably more up to date than those in many European capitals.

An aerial bridge resting on twin towers—
the first of many to span New York's East River.

344 U.S.A. Brooklyn Bridge, the oldest bridge on the East River, New York. Overall length, 2,010 yd

344 Brooklyn Bridge*, begun in 1869, is a perfect example of the romance of these great enterprises in building. Brooklyn, one of the five boroughs of New York, was growing so rapidly that the sixty ferry boat lines were no longer sufficient to handle the daily traffic with Manhattan. Developments in structural steel for bridge-building and in other fields of engineering now made the idea of a bridge across the mile-wide strip of sea, with sufficient clearance above the water to allow ocean-going ships to sail underneath, a feasible proposition.

First the foundations were laid, some distance out in East River, for two piers which would divide the bridge into three spans. The foundations of the piers, a good hundred feet below sea level, were excavated by five hundred men working inside two large caissons with compressed air. A bucket and chain system was used to carry away the debris of the excavations. Next, the masonry of

the piers was built in the open on top of the caissons, which were gradually forced down into the sea bed under the increasing weight. When the caissons had been sunk to the required depth all that remained was to fill them with concrete. In this way the piers were firmly set on an immovable foundation. More than a year was spent in settling the caisson on the Brooklyn side into its proper position. Next, the granite piers themselves were built up to nearly twice the height of the towers of Notre-Dame. 'Labourers working on the scaffolding look like flies caught in a spider's web', 345 wrote the *New York Herald**.

Next, the four huge cables which were to carry the weight of the all-steel bridge, eighty-five feet wide, were strung across the piers. These cables were as thick as a man, each one was plaited from 5,296 steel wires and weighed more than three hundred and fifty tons. The strands had to be twisted when actually in place and

were made first into nineteen secondary cables. The first of these were taken across from one bank to the other under water and hauled up and slung into position when no ships were passing. The bridge was completed in 1883 and its overall length, including the approaches and a central span 535 yards long, was 2,010 yards. It carried four railway tracks, two 346 roads and a footway*.

But tragic shadows overhung the opening ceremonies, for the two engineers had been killed during the building. The elder Roebling had had his foot crushed between two boats and died of tetanus. His son had died of exhaustion after spending too long in the caissons while the foundations were under construction. On the day of the ceremony itself pickpockets, in order to improve their chances, stirred up panic among the fifty thousand spectators massed on the bridge. In the ensuing stampede twenty people were killed and eighty more were injured.

As spiders build their webs,
men spin fine strands of steel to bridge rivers and ravines.

Central span, 535 yds. The supporting cables are 16 ins. thick. The granite towers are 288 ft. high.

345 *Ibid*. Maintenance of the bridge is a job for the strongest heads.

346 *Ibid*. There are four railway lines, two roadways and a raised footpath.

Man's contest with nature is not
a record only of success—trial and error costs lives.

347 Scotland. After the Tay Bridge disaster on December 28th, 1879. Here the cast-iron girders of the old bridge are being cleared at low tide.

On December 28th, 1879, a terrible disaster occurred which sadly marred the triumphal history of Nineteenth Century bridge-building. Two years earlier a British railway company had thrown a bridge across the River Tay, in Scotland, in order to avoid an expensive detour for their trains running between Edinburgh and Dundee. The bridge was two miles long and designed on the same simple principles as many other metal bridges already constructed elsewhere in Britain. None, however, had been quite as long as

the Tay Bridge. The method consisted of a basic structure of cast-iron piles resting on brick piers set in a bed of concrete. On this base the bridge was erected, consisting of eighty-five sections of metal girders each spanning seventy-five yards. The single-track railway line passed eighty feet above sea level.

One stormy night a thousand-yard section of the bridge gave way while a train was passing over it. Eight coaches were swallowed up in the sea as though by magic. Rescuers could find not a trace of

347 the three hundred passengers*. An enquiry was held which revealed faults in the cast-iron girders of the bridge as a result of which they had been incapable of standing up to the unusually high wind and to the vibrations set up by the passage of a train travelling at high speed. Despite public protests the Tay Bridge

348 was promptly rebuilt*, this time with a more resilient iron. The new spans were moved into position on a floating pontoon at high tide and as the tide went out they settled into place on the brick piers.

348 The new Tay Bridge. Nearly two miles long with iron piles. Only a few girders of the old bridge remain.

Rio and Dnieproges

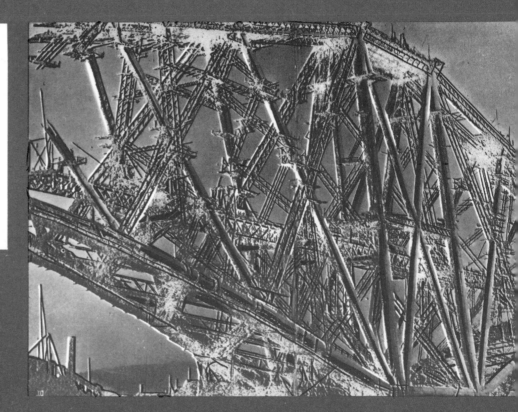

6

the age of confidence

The French and Americans erect a statue
to Liberty which dwarfs even the colossi of Egypt.

The construction of the Statue of
349 Liberty*, on Bedloe's Island at the
entrance to New York harbour, was a
remarkable achievement even in an age
when astonishing feats of engineering
were the order of the day. Its gigantic
proportions suggest the limitless confidence with which technicians were
now accepting the boldest challenges in
the field of construction. Metal structures
had proved their strictly functional utility;
they were yet to be conceived purely with
a view to the spectacular.

A French historian named Laboulaye
had the idea of presenting the city of
New York with a statue to commemorate
the Franco-American alliance during the
War of Independence. He discussed the
project with the sculptor Bartholdi and
commissioned him to design the statue.

The engineer Gustave Eiffel helped
Bartholdi to calculate, in sections, the
measurements of a vast iron skeleton, a
hundred and sixty feet high, which was to
be covered with sheets of copper prepared in advance in the workshops of a
Paris coppersmith. In order to avoid
damage to the statue due to expansion of
the metal or to electrical discharges,
allowance was made for each section to
expand, and insulators were inserted
between the iron framework and the
copper at all points of contact. By making
a series of models, each larger than the
last, they were able to assemble the structure and its covering in Paris once
beforehand. The outer sheath contained
three hundred sheets of copper and
weighed eighty tons.

The entire cost of building the statue,
about $250,000, was raised by a public
subscription in France, without any
assistance from official sources. The
Americans erected a pedestal which
brought the Statue of Liberty's total
height to three hundred and twenty feet.
$125,000 had already been spent when
an enterprising journalist named Joseph
Pulitzer conducted a campaign to raise
the remaining $100,000 needed to com-
plete the project.

The parts of the statue crossed the
Atlantic in two hundred and fourteen
crates and were finally unpacked and
assembled. The inaugural ceremony, on
October 28th, 1886, was presided over by
President Grover Cleveland and attended
by Bartholdi and Ferdinand de Lesseps.

349 New York. Erecting the Statue of Liberty at the harbour entrance.

350 Gustave Eiffel in 1889.

Long before he conceived the tower which was to be the crowning achievement of his career, the engineer Gustave Eiffel* was already an internationally famous specialist in metal construction-work. Because of him metal was used in many structures for which wood and stone would once have been considered indispensable. The bridge he built in 1870 across the River Douro* at Oporto in Portugal had a span of a hundred and seventy-six yards and was a superb example of the possibilities of the metal arch carrying a high-level roadway.

One of Eiffel's boldest strokes was the construction of the Garabit viaduct, across the Truyère Gorge in France. Built between 1880 and 1884, this for long held the record for all single-span bridges in the world. Eiffel's determination to combine beauty with the maximum strength involved him in serious risks. The two sides of the arch reached out into space, in apparent defiance of gravity and supported only by

cables*, until they met in the middle. If particularly high winds had buffeted the bridge before it had been completed disaster would have been inevitable. Yet Eiffel was content to announce that there would be no wind. He was right. Furthermore, he had proved that, even in a technological age, the spirit of adventure was as necessary as ever. When the two sides finally met they formed an arch with a hundred and eighty-yard span, carrying a road bridge five hundred and fifty yards long and four hundred and two feet above the river.

Undeterred by the Tay Bridge disaster, British engineers embarked on the seven-year project of bridging another broad Scottish estuary, that of the Forth. This is a perfect example of a cantilever bridge*, constructed on a system of counter-balancing girders. Each pier provides an anchorage for a pair of cantilevers braced against each other by connecting girders. The cantilevers from adjacent piers reach out towards each other without actually

351 Portugal. Single-span high-level bridge across the Douro at Oporto, built by Gustave Eiffel.

structural uses of metal.

meeting, until a short connecting span is lowered into place, thus enabling the waterway to remain open to shipping while the bridge is in the course of construction. The cantilever towers rise three hundred feet above the Forth and are set in a brick base sunk firmly in the bed of the estuary. The only way in which the brick and concrete foundations could be laid was by submerging huge, four hundred-ton caissons inside which the men could work in safety by electric light.

The Forth Bridge was built simply to carry the railway; in those days road traffic there was very light and crossed the estuary much higher up. As the railway passed a hundred and sixty feet above the river, even the tallest sailing ships could pass underneath. In 1890 two trains, each of which weighed a thousand tons, crossed the one and a half mile long bridge at the same time. The last of the 6,500,000 rivets holding the bridge together was put into place by Edward VII, then Prince of Wales.

352 France. Viaduct of Garabit across the Truyère Gorge under construction.

353 Firth of Forth, Scotland. The Forth Bridge while under construction, before the completion of the central spans.

In Paris, Eiffel builds the
tallest tower in Europe—all of metal.

354 The Eiffel Tower after completion of the second floor in 1889.

355 Painting one of the spiral staircases.

354 The French decided to commemorate the hundredth anniversary of the Revolution by a spectacular Universal Exhibition in Paris. For the occasion Eiffel proposed building a tower* which would afford the most spectacular demonstration of what construction in metal could achieve. The project was commissioned in 1886. Out of a hundred and seven possible sites the Champ de Mars was finally chosen, after a plan to build the tower astride the River Seine had been regretfully abandoned owing chiefly to the need for the firmest possible foundations for the nine thousand ton structure. Eiffel's idea was

to build the first storey to the height of a hundred and eighty-eight feet. Here he envisaged four restaurants and a promenade for two thousand visitors. At three hundred and eighty feet there would be a second storey which would accommodate a post office and a printing press. At nine hundred feet he would build an observation platform for the use of scientists who would, he confidently imagined, turn it to good account. A television transmitter is now installed here. The tower was completed in two years two months, with a scrupulous regard to the schedule. Forty draughts-

men worked on scale drawings of each of the fifteen thousand parts of the edifice for two years. Each part left the factories at Clichy accurate to within a hair's breadth and ready to be fitted into position without further adjustment. Work proceeded at a furious pace in order to be ready for the opening of the Exhibi-

355 tion. The men worked ten hours a day*, even during the hard winter of 1888 when work on all other building had stopped.

356 The second storey* was completed on December 26th, and Gustave Eiffel himself raised the Tricolour at the top on March 31st, 1889.

356 Paris. Perspective view of the Eiffel Tower from the ground

A new source of wealth is tapped as new uses are found for oil.

The origins of the petroleum industry are to be traced back to ancient Mesopotamia, for Noah's ark, the walls of Babylon and the causeways leading to the ziggurats were all built with the aid of pitch or natural asphalt. Incas, Saracens, Chinese, Poles and Alsatians had all used petroleum products in some form, whether for preparing paints or incendiary materials, or for light and heat. The Burmese in the Eighteenth Century were using pipe-lines of lacquered bamboo. But it was not until the Nineteenth Century that oil became a major industry.

In Europe, two Austrian chemists discovered in 1854 that by lightly refining 'naphtha oil' a satisfactory lamp oil could be obtained for domestic purposes. The following year an American chemist,

Samuel M. Kier of Pennsylvania, carried out a similar process. It was necessary, however, to obtain a sufficient supply of the raw material. A railwayman named Drake, also a Pennsylvanian, began boring 357 in Oil Creek Valley near Titusville*, and on August 27th, 1859, he struck oil seventy-five feet below the surface.

A few years later French and English speculators began developing Russian oil-358 fields near Baku* in the Caspian. Rich oil deposits were discovered next in Rumania. From then on the petroleum industry went from strength to strength as the world's oilfields were tapped: Indiana, in 1886; the U.S. Gulf Coast and the Middle East in the early Twentieth Century; Mexico in 1907, and, in 1914, Venezuela.

None of these, however, were to be compared with the oil fever, the 'oil rush' of the first few months after Drake's strike. In the State of Pennsylvania alone, it was estimated that there were soon a thousand well-owners and several hundred refineries. The little town of Oil City, which began as a small river port from which the drums of oil were carried down to Pittsburgh by barge, soon grew to the 359 size and importance of a major city*. Fierce rivalries developed between shippers, carters and rail companies until the railways won, the day they put their tanker-cars into service, although to begin with these were simply a wooden barrel mounted on wheels. But in 1885 the first pipe-line was laid. It was two inches thick and carried the oil five miles, from Oil City to Kittaning. By 1875 the first barges were converted into tankers and travelling down the Alleghany and Ohio rivers.

In 1867 a small grocer named John D. Rockefeller founded the Standard Oil Company. The Royal Dutch company was founded at the Hague in 1890. A few years later the internal combustion engine and the automobile industry had done for oil-rich country what the steam-engine had done for coal-bearing regions; instead of slag heaps, this time it 360 was oil-derricks*.

357 U.S.A. Titusville, Pennsylvania. Drake, in the top hat, standing beside his oil well.

358 Russia. Oil well at Baku in the XIXth C.

359 U.S.A. Street in Oil City, Pennsylvania. Oil drums on their way to Pittsburgh during the first great oil rush.

360 U.S.A. Forest of oil derricks at Signal Hill, California. One of the richest of the early XIXth C. oilfields.

361 London. Sectional view of the Thames Embankment at the end of the XIXth C. showing: 1. water mains; 2. sewer; 3. underground railway.

By the latter half of the Nineteenth Century influx into the capitals of Europe had reached saturation point and it became essential to open new traffic arteries. London was the first city forced by growing congestion to find some quick, practicable means of transporting the million or so suburban dwellers from the main-line termini where they arrived every day to and from their destinations in the centre of town. The first underground line, the Inner Circle, was in fact built to link the railway termini. On January 18th, 1863, thirty thousand Londoners tried out the three miles of underground railway built between

361 Paddington and Farringdon. In the year that followed more than nine million people travelled underground. In 1869 the already crowded substratum of London* had to make room for yet another underground railway, the 'tube'. This proved unsuccessful at first owing to the failure of the cable haulage system, but twenty years later the invention of electric motors made the scheme a feasible one.

362 The Paris metro* was not inaugurated until 1900 but its beginnings were more ambitious: its first line ran ten miles through Paris, from Vincennes to the Porte Maillot, and made a good axis from

which to extend lines to the suburbs.

In London the underground lines, apart from the very earliest, all run very deep but in Paris the principle was to

363 keep them as near the surface as possible*, and to have both lines in the same tiled tunnel. But the technicians were faced with a problem at the five points at which the various lines had to cross the Seine. Their final solution was to construct

364 cylinders* to be sunk into the river bed, or alternatively metal shields which could be pushed out under the river bed from beneath either bank while the earth was cut away in front of them. If the mud was too liquid, it first had to be frozen.

achieved underground.

363 Paris. Cutting through the Rue de Rivoli during the construction of the 'Concorde' metro station.

364 Paris. Metal caisson under construction to carry the metro under the Seine.

362 Paris. Metro tunnel and platform in 1900.

A metal framework and a solid foundation
permits builders their first experiments with the skyscraper.

365 New York. Elevated railway tracks on either side of the Bowery.

366 New York. A train on the elevated railway. Late XIXth C.

In New York, where the problem of transport was also becoming acute, the idea of underground railways was abandoned as being too time-consuming a project, in favour of an overhead railway, the more feasible in that the avenues were broad and straight*. The trains ran twenty feet above the main arteries of the city, on a scaffolding of cast-iron girders*, so that the noise and the smoke they caused may be imagined! This, however, deterred no one. In the year 1882, ninety million passengers travelled on the sixty miles of track. Little by little the noisy and unsightly 'elevated' gave place to the modern 'subway' system.

By 1898, when Manhattan was bursting at the seams, the New York boroughs of Brooklyn, Queens and the Bronx were all linked with it over the rivers. The Williamsburg Bridge, with its six railway tracks, two roadways and two footpaths, was opened in 1903. In 1909 came the Queensborough Bridge, with four railway tracks and six roads, and Manhattan Bridge, with eight railway tracks and four roads.

All these bridges were built of metal, and metal construction was to be the final answer to a problem which was rapidly getting out of hand. With no room for expansion the only alternative was to build upwards. The origins of the skyscraper are so complex that it is impossible to attribute the invention to any one person. As early as 1854 an architect with a passion for iron structures erected a building without the usual masonry walls for a New York publishing house. The entire façade was made up of pillars which supported the floors and almost all the space between them was filled in with glass. The same principle was adopted by the architects of skyscrapers: exceptionally tall buildings supported not by their walls but by a metal skeleton*.

The claim to have originated the metal frame building was advanced by one Buffington of Minneapolis, but this claim was disputed by W. Le Baron Jenney, who in 1885 built the Home Insurance Building in Chicago. Whatever the rights of the case, it was the group of architects known as 'the Chicago school', and especially Louis Sullivan, who played a major part in the invention of the skyscraper proper. Among the Chicago school's innovations were the systematic use of metal frameworks, the develop-

365

366

367

367 New York. Flatiron Building. Early XXth C. skyscraper.

368 New York. The *New York Times* building, erected in 1905.

ment of floating foundations to enable tall buildings to be set on marshy ground, and the pioneering of the apartment blocks, which were against the American preference for individual homes. They were responsible, too, for much of the closer collaboration between architects and engineers which later produced the austere functional styles of the 'twenties and 'thirties.

For some time yet, though, New Yorkers would be able to revel in their Gothic belfries, Renaissance domes, their pillars and turrets and even more fan-
368 tastic creations★. The design of the 790-foot high Woolworth Building, opened by President Wilson in 1913, earned for it the nickname of 'the cathedral of commerce'. Passers-by were amazed to see the metal skeleton of the Flatiron
367 Building★ completed before the lower

floors were even begun. All the steel girders were in place long before the walls were more than a shell, a sight common enough today but a good deal more startling fifty years ago.

Although architects contrived to step back the upper floor of their skyscrapers there were some, like the Equitable Building, which presented an unbroken vertical façade of thirty-eight floors. In 1916 it became necessary to pass a Zoning Law, controlling the height of buildings according to the width of the streets, in order to preserve any remnants of light and air for those on the ground.

As the business quarter of the city became concentrated at the southern end of Manhattan Island, so the price of land down there rose to astronomical figures. It was no wonder that, after paying thousands upon thousands of dollars for a

few square yards of land, builders exploited their property to the limits of their powers—vertically. Even in cities where shortage of space did not make the skyscraper an economic necessity, the building of skyscrapers was still undertaken because they could be erected so fast. Although the laying of the foundations may have been more crucial and complicated and therefore have taken longer than in other forms of building, once this had been accomplished the metal structure could be run up at phenomenal speed. Even in those early years, the skeleton of the twelve-storey block built for a newspaper, the *Baltimore American*, was erected in five and a half months. The four hundred-foot Farmers Bank Building in Pittsburgh, containing five thousand tons' worth of iron girders, was achieved in six months.

On the West Coast
San Francisco gives a lead in bridge-building.

San Francisco wanted to become the queen of America's west coast, and in 1905 she built the two mile long Oakland 369 Bridge★, one of the longest in the world, to rival any of those in New York. Six thousand workers were employed in building the bridge, and nearly two hundred thousand tons of steel and cables and a hundred and sixty-three thousand tons of concrete were used in its construction. The bridge crossed the bay of San Francisco, using the islet of Yerba Buena in the middle of the bay as a stepping-stone.

It was in 1905, too, that the United States brought the long history of the 370 Panama Canal★ to its conclusion. No sooner was the Suez Canal open to shipping than de Lesseps began to think about a canal through the isthmus of Panama. At this point a neck of land fifty miles thick separated the Pacific and Atlantic Oceans, as a result of which shipping was faced with a twelve thousand mile detour round the tip of South America. Initially two main obstacles stood in the way of the project. First, the Americans wanted to build the canal through Nicaragua while the French had already opened negotiations with Columbia, of which Panama was then a part; and second, de Lesseps had envi-

saged a canal at sea level, similar to Suez, which would have avoided the need for locks but would have involved excavating whole mountains of rock. In 1880 work began on the canal. Forty thousand Negro and Indian labourers were employed by the twenty companies, of all nationalities, who undertook the job. In 1886 they started to level the rocky outcrop of Culebra, but in four years the height of the three hundred-foot bluff had been reduced by only ten or twelve feet. Then Eiffel, who had been in favour of locks from the beginning, was given the task of revising the plans. But it was too late. Yellow fever decimated the

369 U.S.A. Oakland Bridge, California, which crosses San Francisco Bay in two hops by way of the small island of Yerba Buena.

Mountains are levelled, locks built, and ships can sail over the Isthmus of Panama.

workers and then came a financial crash which stopped work altogether.

Another Frenchman, however, Bunau-Varilla, returned to the attack, persuading the Americans to abandon their Nicaraguan scheme and to pay for the work. In 1903 he himself financed the *pronunciamento* which brought into being the new independent state of Panama. Work on the canal was resumed under the direction of the American army and with the strictest health regulations. A system of enormous linked locks was built all along the Culebra* and ships were hauled along each three hundred yard stretch by locomotives. These engines* were a distinct innovation: they were small, powerful, and electrically operated. By 1910, fifty thousand men were employed on the project and all the latest technological developments contributed to speed the work. On August 3rd, 1914, the *Cristobal* negotiated the fifty-mile sea passage through the isthmus.

The Corinth Canal is undoubtedly less important than that of Panama, but it has the distinction of having taken the longest time to build. The idea of cutting a canal through the isthmus of Corinth to link the Ionian and Aegean seas and thus avoid the perilous sea journey round the jagged Peloponnesian coast dated back to pre-Roman times. The Emperor Nero, wielding a golden spade, had lifted the first shovelful and inaugurated the work: but it was not until 1893 that the four-mile canal was finally open to shipping.

371 Panama Canal. Cutting a way through the rocky massif of Culebra.

372 Panama Canal. Electric traction engines on the lock side at Miraflores.

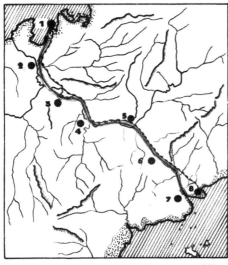

370 The Panama Canal. 1. Colon; 2. 1st siding; 3. 2nd siding; 4. 3rd siding; 5. 4th siding; 6. Culebra; 7. 5th siding; 8. Panama.

The Zeppelin, Leviathan of the air, competes with the ocean liner in size and speed.

373 France. The launching of the transatlantic liner *France* from Penhoët shipyards. 720 ft long. Built to carry 2,000 passengers.

374 The ill-fated liner *Titanic* in 1912.

In spite of the failure of the *Great Eastern* (see page 170), the late Nineteenth and early Twentieth Centuries saw the great maritime powers vying with each other to build the biggest and fastest liners to put on the Atlantic run. The 373 23,600 ton liner *France** was launched in 1911 from the Penhoët shipyards. She had a seven hundred and twenty-foot hull, steel-built, and her four turbines developed forty-five thousand horse-power.

At the same time British, American and German shipyards were trying out new answers to old problems; they replaced iron with steel, installed stabilisers, and gained greater efficiency with the use of fuel oil and the triple expansion turbines.

The coveted Blue Riband, for the fastest passenger crossing of the North Atlantic, was first awarded in 1900. The length of the pennant, which was flown at the masthead of the victorious ship, corresponded in metres to the vessel's speed in knots. Its first holders were the Germans with the *Deutschland* (23 knots) and then with the *Kaiser Wilhelm II* (also 23 knots) in 1904. They lost the trophy to Britain, who held it and increased her lead nine times, with the *Lusitania* and the *Mauretania*. The torpedoing of the *Lusitania* on May 7th, 1915, caused the death of twelve hundred

375 Germany. Airship under construction. The aluminium framework of the 780 ft. long airship known as the *Graf Zeppelin*.

374 passengers and brought the United States into the war. Two other British ships, the ill-fated *Titanic**, which hit an iceberg on her maiden voyage, and the *Olympic* were the longest in the world.

The super-liners were threatened at this time with competition from another fast-moving monster—the airship. In 1896 a retired German cavalry officer, Count von Zeppelin, began the pro-
375 duction of these giant airships* with rigid metal frameworks built of a new, lightweight metal alloy called aluminium.
376 The *Graf Zeppelin** which flew from Germany to America in 1928 was seven hundred and eighty feet long and

powered by five motors. The journey took a hundred and eleven hours and the airship carried a crew of thirty-seven, eighteen passengers and sixty-two thousand letters. The following year the *Graf Zeppelin* went round the world, crossing the Pacific Ocean in sixty-nine hours and the Atlantic in sixty-seven. When it finally died—of old age—in 1937, it had travelled a total distance of 1,031,250 miles. But a terrible disaster put an end to the great exploits of these giants of the sky. In 1937 the biggest and fastest of them all, the *Hindenburg*, which had room for seventy-five passengers, crashed with a loss of thirty-five lives.

376 The *Graf Zeppelin* at Tempelhof airfield in 1934.

Rio—a modern city
in a superb setting.

377 Rio* was founded by the Portuguese in
1567 on the shores of a magnificent bay
almost ninety miles round. The growth
of the city was for a long time limited to
a narrow strip of marshy ground at the
foot of precipitous hills. As early as 1910,
however, a metropolis of the Twentieth
Century was already taking shape. A main
avenue, thirty yards wide and bordered
by pavements of black and white mosaic,
was driven straight through the old
quarter of the town. Built along this
Avenida Rio Branco were theatres, hotels,
museums, libraries—all the distinguishing
features of a capital. After the First
World War, which left the city unscathed,
Rio undertook further developments.

In 1930 the Avenida Rio Branca was
superseded by the Avenida Presidente
Vargas. Hundreds of dwellings were
demolished to make way for this new
street, a hundred yards wide, which
included three separate traffic lanes in
each direction, one each for trams, buses
and private cars.

378 The following year, a statue of Christ*,
a hundred feet high, by the French
sculptor Landowski was erected on a rock
dominating the city. The figure stands
with outspread arms, looking out over the
city streets towards the vast bay with its
green islands and its ceaseless traffic of
liners, cargo ships and coasters. At the
same period the famous Copacabana
beach was only a deserted, unfashionable
suburb of the city. Once a road tunnel
had been driven through the intervening
spur of rock, Copacabana became a
popular resort. Buildings of every shape
and size began to dot the coast: medieval
crenellated castles, Elizabethan manors,
Venetian palazzi, Moorish mosques, a
building boom in fancy dress. Land along
the sea front became as valuable as in
Manhattan, and a fringe of skyscrapers
grew up along Copacabana beach.

The city continued to grow throughout
the Second World War. Brazilian architects learned from European masters such
as Gropius, Mies van der Rohe and Le
Corbusier and, with generous support
from the State, embarked on an ambitious
building programme. A whole school of
Brazilian architects set about erecting
office blocks and government buildings,
museums, theatres, giant blocks of flats,
hotels, banks and factories that put their
country among the foremost architectural
innovators in the world.

377–378 Brazil. Bay of Rio de Janeiro; the Christ
of Mt Corcovado in the foreground.

Prefabricated at the steel works, erected in the heart of town, the giant skyscraper rises at a dizzying speed.

During the opening decades of the Twentieth Century, the skyline of Manhattan was graced by several thick clusters of skyscrapers built, often, in a
379 style reminiscent of an earlier age*. The clean, streamlined silhouette of the Empire State Building, started in 1929, was something of an innovation. Its foundations were laid along one of the busiest stretches of Fifth Avenue, and its hundred and two floors, bringing the building to a height of 1250 feet, were to overtop any building in existence. The greater part of a city block had first to be cleared, the foundations excavated and the new giant erected without any interruption of the traffic flowing past the site. No materials could be stored on the site and all the steel girders were brought direct from the factories at Pittsburgh
380 and assembled in mid-air**, less than four
381 days after they were made. The Empire State Building was constructed at a fantastic speed; fourteen and a half floors were completed within ten days.

The first truck drew up beside the buildings which were to be demolished on October 1st, 1929, and on May 1st, 1931, the Empire State Building was formally opened. It has six thousand four hundred windows and contains sixty-seven lifts. The express elevators take less than a minute to get from street level up to the eightieth floor.

Many people predicted the collapse of this modern Tower of Babel. But it stood firm, even when a large aircraft crashed into the seventy-ninth floor one day in a thick fog. Thirteen people lost their lives and twenty-five were injured, but the building suffered no serious damage.

The entire building is taken up by offices, shops and restaurants, and so many thousands of people work there that their hours have to be staggered to avoid a bottleneck in the elevator service. The building was constructed during the heyday of the airships and a terminal was added with the idea of providing an anchorage for the craft. None ever used it.

380 Workman giving signal to hoist a girder.

381 Empire State Building under construction; to avoid congestion in the street, all building materials are lifted into place on reaching the site.

◄ 379 New York. View of skyscrapers from the East River.

207

Where fertile fields are more precious than anchovy fisheries land is reclaimed from the sea.

382–383 Holland. Medemblik. Above: the eleven-mile dyke during construction in 1927. Below: In 1930, after completion.

Motorists speed across the Zuyderzee.

At the beginning of the present century the island of Urk, off the Dutch coast, was the home of a small, patriarchal community of anchovy-fishermen. It lay in the centre of a broad gulf created by a terrible flood tide in the Thirteenth Century. Today Urk lies in the middle of a flourishing agricultural region. Around it are 120,000 acres of fertile land growing corn, beet and potatoes, and giving a livelihood to sixty thousand people.

The struggle against the sea had been the main preoccupation of the Dutch people for seven centuries. The idea of draining the Zuyderzee was first envisaged in the Fifteenth Century, but it took an engineer like Cornelius Lely (1854–1929) to put the idea into practice**. After years of disappointments Lely was given a free hand by the queen to deal with the problem of controlling the sea. His idea was to build an immense dyke, twenty miles long, closing off the Zuyderzee at its narrowest point. In the shelter of this dyke, the low-lying *polders* could be divided into sections, drained, and provided with roads, canals and irrigation ditches. Work was only begun on June 29th, 1920, but a high degree of mechanisation shortened the estimated schedule considerably. The convex-shaped dyke was constructed by sinking two parallel rows of huge wicker caissons ballasted with stones. Powerful dredgers equipped with pumps forced huge quantities of sand into the intervening trench. On top of this foundation, basalt blocks were laid in position and held together with a particularly binding local clay and frames of willow faggots. Finally, the top of the dyke was surfaced with earth and sown with grass seed to anchor the soil against the wind. A

382
383

385 The current pouring through the great dyke before it was closed, May 1932.

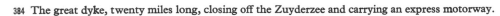

384 The great dyke, twenty miles long, closing off the Zuyderzee and carrying an express motorway.

384 motor road* could then be constructed along the top of the dyke.

The most dramatic moment of the whole undertaking came in October 1930 during preparations for closing the last gap when a storm threatened to carry away a large part of the dyke. Every available boat, whether it had a motor, sail or oars, was pressed into service to bring earth and stones. For hours the waters piled through the breach but eventually the passage was sealed. In May 1932, the dyke was finished and the sea tides no longer entered the Zuyderzee*.

385

209

The new Russia needs power: hydro-electric power.
She harnesses the waters of her broadest rivers.

386 U.S.S.R. Materials arriving by train during building of the Dnieproges Dam in 1930.

387–388 Dnieproges nearing completion. The dam, 836 yds.

In the new Russia which succeeded the revolution of 1917, political and economic ends tended to coincide. Lenin gave the word for Russia to 'catch up with the capitalist nations and then over-take them'. His definition of Communism was 'the power of the Soviets plus the electrification of the entire land'. The *Goëlro*, Lenin's plan for complete electri-fication within ten or fifteen years, was inaugurated in 1920 while Russia was still in the throes of civil war.

Russia was at that time in the doldrums, economically speaking, and the execution of these development programmes became a basic creed to which the entire nation was forced to subscribe. Stalin kept up the relentless pressure with absolute confidence in the goal. In 1928 he launched the first Five Year Plan which listed essential objectives, stated certain fixed aims and directed labour and economic resources accordingly. This Five Year Plan of 1928–32 was conducted

along almost military lines. The shortage of technicians still precluded the use of mechanisation on any great scale and in these days much of the work was done by human labour in the face of great diffi-culties, especially that of finding enough food for the workers. Forty-four per cent of private industry had already been collectivised by 1928. The transformation was completed by 1932. The *kolkhoz*, or collective farm, and the even larger State Farm known as a *Sovkhoz*, was substituted for the innumerable small holdings, often with brutal suddenness.

Canals were dug from the Baltic to the White Sea through Lake Onega, and from Moscow to the Volga by the Moskva River. In 1932 Professor Schmidt sailed from Archangel to Vladivostok by way of the Arctic Ocean, thus linking the extremities of the Soviet Union by a northern sea route. A fleet of fourteen cargo ships, escorted by ice-breakers, thereafter proved the possibility of a regu-

lar summer traffic between the two ports; an immense no-man's-land was open to development.

With a realistic appraisal of his needs, Stalin called in the help of foreign technicians, German and American in particular, to supervise many of his most ambitious projects.

American expertise contributed to the building of a huge tractor plant at Stalingrad, a car-manufacturing city at Gorki, formerly Nijni-Novgorod, and the Dnieper Dam***, which was to be the biggest in Europe. The dam supplied hydro-electric power to the first industrial 'combine' of modern times, providing a living for sixteen million people and in-volving seven major industries—steel, coke, aluminium, refractories, cement, engineering and chemical fertilisers. Moreover, the dam made it possible to irrigate a barren area of land the size of the British Isles. Twenty thousand young labourers built it in ten years.

386
387
388

In the shadow of the dam,
lands are irrigated, industries founded.

long and 122 ft. high, directs the flow of the stream through sluice gates. Below: the opening ceremony on May 1st, 1932.

As prospectors discover rich mineral deposits, the barren wastes of Siberia are opened up.

389 U.S.S.R. The site of Magnitogorsk in 1929, with geologists' and builders' camp.

390 Magnitogorsk in 1933. View of coke works supplied from the Kuznetsk coal mines.

The Trans-Siberian Railway, opened in 1903, put Vladivostok only seventeen days' journey from Hamburg. The line was 4,638 miles long and was a proof that already under the Tsars Siberia was being opened up. Under Stalin the region became a veritable industrial empire. Ambitious projects were undertaken for the systematic development of five major industries: coal, chemicals and potassium products, copper and petroleum.

The site of the most impressive of these projects was the hill of Magnitnaïa in the Southern Urals, which contained rich iron ore deposits. When the first

389 pioneers set up their tents* in the steppe around the foot of the hill, eleven engineers from Cleveland were among them. They built one of the largest industrial plants in the world, the Magnitostroy, and around it grew up the

390 town of Magnitogorsk*. A twelve hundred and fifty-mile railway was specially constructed to link this iron town with the coal-mining centre of Kuznetsk, at the foot of the Altaï Mountains. Cities sprang up like mushrooms. Kirovsk in the north, well within the Arctic circle, is a characteristic example. The first inhabitants were geologists living in three tents, in 1923. By 1935 Kirovsk had fifty thousand inhabitants and was a centre for the mining of rare metals. In 1956 the population had grown to 211,000, and Kirovsk superseded Murmansk as the most important city within the Arctic Circle. The inhabitants of this northern latitude had a problem adopting themselves to the climate and obtaining supplies. From 1938 onwards Stalin

391 U.S.S.R. Construction work on the Fergana Canal, Uzbekistan, which brought water 180 miles from the Naryn river to irrigate the desert regions.

envisaged the likelihood of war and kept his Siberian projects a close secret.

391 The great Fergana canal* in the Muslim republic of Uzbekistan, in central Asia, was begun in 1939. The two hundred thousand workers engaged on building the canal were organised like an army. In forty-five days they shifted fourteen million cubic metres of earth and cut forty-five supplementary irrigation canals. When the canal was ready, drainage, irrigation and protection against soil erosion soon made Uzbekistan a wealthy province. The waters of the River Naryn flowed down the Fergana canal along whose a hundred and eighty miles ships could now carry cargoes of tea, cotton, fruit and vegetables to a region that had been arid desert for centuries.

After the German invasion, when a great part of Russia's industry fell back towards the eastern provinces, the Trans-Siberian and the Turksib railways took on a vital importance. The 2,200 mile

392 long Turksib line*, linking Siberia with Russian Turkestan and the Caucasus, was laid between 1927 and 1930. It was necessary to connect these two rich areas of the U.S.S.R. in order to encourage the expansion of cotton growing and to exploit to the full the vast resources of Kazakhstan. The work was estimated to take four years, but was finished in three. The existence of another line across eastern Siberia, the 1500 mile Baikal-Amour-Magistral, was not known until many years later; although the line was built between 1933 and 1942 there has never been any mention of it on maps or official documents.

392 U.S.S.R. Opening of the Turkestan–Siberia Railway in 1930.

213

In its underground railway
Moscow expresses its taste for luxury.

393 Moscow. A corridor of the underground, showing marble floor and chandeliers.

394 Moscow. Escalators—one up and two down—on the underground during rush hour.

As the capital of a nation which prides itself on its great building achievements, Moscow boasts an exceptionally fine underground railway. In May 1935 huge posters appeared on every wall in the city announcing: *Yet Metro!* (We have the metro!), and the people of Moscow hailed their new acquisition as 'the Eighth Wonder of the World'. In fact the Moscow underground is a remarkable construction. It is a subterranean palace 393 of polished marble* with huge, brilliantly lighted stations decorated with statues, pillars, bas-reliefs and paintings by the foremost Soviet artists. The platforms are all very deep down and are reached by 394 escalators* which have carried two hundred thousand people a day to and from the comfortable, silent trains ever since 1935. The luxury of the underground may provide the people of Moscow with some compensation for the poor living conditions which have been general in the city. The first section to be opened was some seven and a half miles long, and this was built in three years, with materials brought from all over the Soviet Union. The Russians compare this achievement proudly with the four to fifteen years which it took to build lines of comparable distance in London, Berlin and Paris.

None the less the engineers had a hard struggle against the shifting and waterlogged subsoil, which still presents a constant problem to those working under the city of Moscow. Even during the war years work on the Moscow underground was continued, providing transport for workers to and from the factories situated near the original routes. From 1938, three diagonal lines carried a million passengers per day. In 1949 the expansion of the metro reached colossal proportions with the projected construction of a great underground circle line to pass through eighteen suburbs and connect all the seven mainline stations.

Ultra-modern equipment for the powerful ventilation system and foolproof automatic points were supplied by a number of factories in Moscow, Leningrad, the Ukraine and the Urals. The most famous architects contributed to the building of the stations: each was designed in a different style in accordance with a given ideological theme. The *Komsomolskaia Circuit* station, for example, was inspired by the great Soviet victories during the 1939–1945 war.

Essen
and An Shan

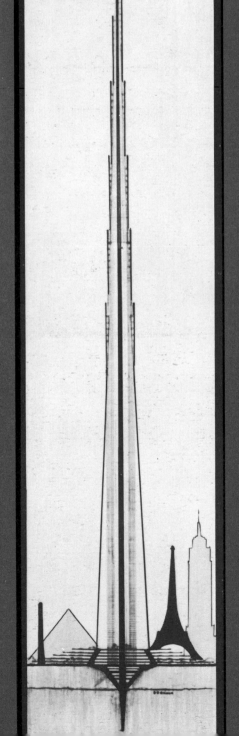

7

all
the
world
a work-
shop

Giant liners race each other
across the Atlantic to capture the Blue Riband.

Although as often as not, by this stage, the impetus behind the great works of construction being undertaken the world over sprang from the need to combat famine, disease and climatic conditions, we must not pass over one or two achievements born of earlier rivalries. On the eve of the Second World War the great transatlantic shipping companies were still in keen competition for the Blue Riband of the Atlantic (see page 202). From 1929 onwards this trophy had been held successively by the German liners *Bremen* and *Europa* and then by the 395 Italian *Rex* before the *Normandie** won it back for France. But in 1938 France lost it to the *Queen Mary*, who made the crossing at a speed of 31 knots. Her 396 sister ship the *Queen Elizabeth*** is still 397 the largest passenger liner in the world although she is not as fast as the present holder of the Blue Riband, the American liner *United States*, which can develop a speed approaching 36 knots.

395 France. The 83,000 ton liner *Normandie* under construction in 1934.

396–397 Gt. Britain. The stern and one of the screws of the liner *Queen Elizabeth* (85,000 tons), launched in 1938.

The Great Dictators enrich their capitals with splendid public works.

During the 1930's international rivalry gradually assumed a less peaceful aspect. In Italy and Germany growth and expansion in the face of all economic and financial difficulties became necessary to the life of the regime. The size of its achievements was a measure of national pride and ambition. Moreover, the mobilisation of the resources of industry and labour made these grandiose projects (many of which had in fact been planned under a previous regime) a practical possibility.

The centre of Rome was still almost impassable for modern traffic, and a vast wealth of archaeological remains lay hidden beneath its medieval huddle of mean dwellings. In 1932, Mussolini adopted a plan devised as early as 1911 and set an army of six thousand labourers to work clearing a passage through one of the medieval quarters of the city. In a bare eleven months they had built the broad Via dell' Impero* between Piazza Venezia and the Colosseum. The rest of Europe was amazed at the speed with which the Italian dictator set about draining the Pontine marshes outside Rome. In February 1931 a law was passed giving old soldiers the right to settle in an area comprising a hundred square miles of unhealthy marshland which until then had been given over to cattle and gorse bushes. By 1932 Littoria, the first town in the area, was founded. Land was cleared, roads and drainage canals built, incorporating a system of secondary channels and outfalls. Next, the soil was purified and farms started. Within three years of this stage land which had been deserted for two thousand years was supporting two thousand farms and cottages, a hundred and eighty miles of roads, over eight hundred of canals, fourteen villages and two towns.

It was in 1925 that the Fascist regime built the first dual-carriage *autostrada*. It was still far too narrow, but it did run almost dead straight for many miles with scarcely any dangerous junctions or crossings. Here was the prototype of the great motorways of the Twentieth Century. Ten years later Adolf Hitler took up the idea in Germany on a larger scale, with the *autobahn*. German engineers had already been studying the problems of road transport and had built a motorway from Cologne to Bonn; when Hitler came to power he took advantage of this initiative to promote a major road net-

398 Italy. Rome. Building the Via dell' Impero, from the Colosseum to the monument of Victor Emmanuel.

399 Germany. Crowds at the 1936 Olympic Games in Berlin. Picture taken from the airship *Hindenburg*.

Where the Trocadéro once stood
the Palais de Chaillot rises beside the Seine.

400 U.S.A. Heads of four American presidents carved out of Mount Rushmore.

401 Paris. Work on the Palais de Chaillot and the gardens in preparation for the Universal Exhibition of 1937.

work. Partly as a measure to prevent unemployment, and also in part to prepare the way for his armies' invasion of Europe, Hitler turned a labour force of a hundred and twenty thousand men onto the roads. Poorly equipped with picks and shovels, they built fourteen hundred miles of fast motor roads. As a diversion, he also built a stadium for the 1936 Olympic Games in Berlin which was the biggest of its time*.

In a world where great, symbolic monuments were once again coming into fashion the United States had their own strange creation at Mount Rushmore*, where immense stone heads of the founders of American democracy were carved out of the living rock.

The Paris Exhibition of 1937, at the foot of the Eiffel Tower, was intended to carry a message of confidence to the world by showing men the arts and sciences that were not subject to any barriers of race or civilisation or political opinions. The Palais de Chaillot* was built on the site of the 1878 Trocadéro (see page 180). The new building consisted of a pair of enormous curved wings over two hundred yards long, situated between two monumental pavilions. In the basement a theatre was built to seat two thousand. The building was faced with limestone over a concrete infrastructure.

Concrete was also used extensively in other nearby buildings such as the Musée d'Art Moderne and the Musée des Travaux Publics, but it was not until after the war that many public buildings in Paris, such as the UNESCO building, relied principally on concrete.

The idea of using iron as a reinforcement for concrete was first thought of by Fairbairn in 1845. The mixture of cement sand and gravel thus reinforced was developed initially as a method of prefabricating girders. Engineers began to use it in building bridges and aqueducts. Then architects adopted it and began building flats, slaughter-houses, even a church in concrete. Among early concrete buildings were the Queen Alexandra Sanatorium at Davos in Switzerland, built in 1907, and the warehouses of Montgomery Ward and Co. in Chicago. The development of concrete reinforced with steel rather than with iron, and the subsequent development of pre-stressed concrete, was to open up a whole new field of architectural possibilities.

399
400
401

402 New York. Rockefeller Center: Fifteen buildings on the former site of two hundred houses.

Rockefeller Center, a model of planned development,

Steel and concrete came as a boon to the developers of Manhattan Island, where the shortage of building space was presenting even more of a problem, but where the bedrock of the island was a solid granite capable of supporting any structure. Today the most homogeneous architectural development in the centre of the city is made up of the fifteen towering buildings of Rockefeller 402 Center*. The concrete foundations of some of these buildings go down a hundred feet into the ground. The total framework, held together by two million rivets, weighs 138,000 tons. The cranes which hauled up the elements of the building were fixed onto the framework and moved up from floor to floor as the work progressed. The walls and floors are of reinforced concrete, fitted into this framework, and much of the wall space is taken up by the 16,500 windows. Inside the buildings are hundreds of miles of lead pipes, thousands of miles of electric wiring, twenty-eight thousand telephones, and two hundred and fifteen lifts, the swiftest of which climb at a rate of twenty-five feet per second. In this space barely two hundred and fifty yards square there are twenty-two consulates, twenty-four restaurants, six schools and eleven hundred business offices. Thirty-two thousand people work here, and a hundred and thirty thousand visit the premises every day.

In this world of giant undertakings nothing seemed impossible. The Chicago River was even made to run backwards 403 into the Mississippi* for reasons of hygiene. Sites became so vast that the building trade was organised into a series of monster combines.

The choice of a permanent home for the 404 United Nations in New York* involved three years' intensive study and consultation by some of the greatest modern architects of all nationalities, including Le Corbusier, Niemeyer, Sven Markelius, Vladimir Bordiansky, Matthew Nowicki and Josef Havalicek. The contract was eventually awarded to the firm of Harrison and Abramovitz. The main building has thirty-nine floors and rises to a height of 505 feet above street level, though it is 387 feet long and only 73 feet wide. On the other hand, it is faced almost entirely with glass—5,400 windows in all—and constitutes a new look in architecture: buildings without walls.

403 Chicago. The Chicago River diverted to flow back into the Mississippi.

replaces a jumble of small dwellings with fifteen towering blocks of masonry.

404 New York. The United Nations Secretariat Building. The building is 505 ft. high, with 39 floors of offices and 5,400 windows.

The Tennessee Valley Authority
builds thirty dams to supply power for industry.

405 U.S.A. Hoover Dam on the Colorado River (720 ft. high).

407 U.S.A. Tennessee Valley Authority: the Hiwassee Dam (300 ft. high).

405 President Roosevelt's New Deal policy of 1933 made a programme of great engineering projects an essential part of the fight for full employment and for his nation's recovery after the economic slump. The Boulder Dam*, now known as the Hoover Dam, on the borders of Arizona and Nevada, speeded up the industrialisation of California and made possible the development of huge areas of unfertile land. The dam, whose total mass is a million tons heavier than that of the tallest pyramid, is 726 feet high and almost as thick at its foot. It is 1,244 feet long and contains 4,400,000 cubic yards of concrete.

The highly paid and extremely skilled workers engaged on the project first bored diversion tunnels through the rock, and 406 erected trash-screens to prevent the rubble from the diggings being carried down the Colorado River, a process which came into wide use in subsequent undertakings*. Next, the dam itself was built in hundred-foot sections. When the dam was ready, one of America's great transcontinental roads used it, appropriately enough, as a bridge across the river.

But huge as it was, the Hoover Dam was surpassed even before completion by a scheme on an even vaster scale. This was the work of the Tennessee Valley Authority which was established to develop and exploit the whole of the Tennessee River Valley for navigational, hydro-electric, flood-control and other purposes. It is still the largest scheme of its kind anywhere in the world. The T.V.A. was responsible to Roosevelt alone, and, using enormous resources of public money, it set about controlling the river by means of thirty dams, like the 407 Hiwassee Dam*, over an area of 696,000 acres. Two hundred thousand workers were employed on the construction of the new dams. The main by-product of the work of the T.V.A. was hydro-electricity. In 1960 the scheme produced 11,385,460 kilowatts, of which 33% came from hydro-electric installations and 67% from coal plants. The T.V.A. is now the largest coal consumer in the U.S. and absorbs some eighteen million tons per year. Electricity from the Tennessee Valley is used by 150 municipal and rural systems as well as in private industries and those run by the T.V.A.

406 U.S.A. Glen Canyon Dam on the Colorado River, Arizona. Building a trash screen. ➤

**Poised high above San Francisco Bay—
the Golden Gate Bridge, one of the most graceful in the world.**

408 U.S.A. Grand Coulee Dam on the Columbia River, Washington.

409 U.S.A. Steel and concrete irrigation pipe passing under a stream and a railway line.

408 The Grand Coulee Dam* on the Columbia River, which flows through a succession of superb canyons and falls in the north-west corner of the United States, broke several records. It was built by the U.S. Bureau of Reclamations, and 10,585,000 cubic yards of rubble and concrete went into its construction— more than the total volume of the walls of 25,000 seven-storey buildings. In order to prevent seepage whole rivers of cement grouting had to be injected into its foundations. The dam is 550 feet high and 4,173 feet along the crest, letting through a sheet of water whose force has been calculated at thirty million horse-power. Such is the force of water coming through the sluices that it has to be canalised at the foot of the dam by means of a concave wall built of cement. The reservoir, above the dam, has a capacity of 9,402,000 acre-feet. It makes use of a natural fault hollowed out by the Columbia river and left dry when the river returned to its old channel after the ice age. The town of Coulee grew up on the borders of this lake to house the fifteen thousand workers on the project. The instability of the soil, which contained 25% water, threatened to bring the work to a permanent halt; a solution was found, though, by injecting chilled brine through hundreds of tubes, into the shifting mass of earth.

The dam was finally completed in 1942 after more than seven years' work, and an installed power capacity of 1,974,000 kilowatts made it the most powerful generator in the world. It also serves to irrigate the arid areas of the state of Washington, as well as for flood control and water supply. Huge steel and con-

409 crete pipes* carry water under streams, roads and railways, and distribute it through thousands of secondary channels.

410 The Golden Gate Bridge* across the mouth of San Francisco Bay is one of the wonders of the modern world. It is the longest suspension bridge ever built, with a span of 1,540 yards between the towers. The master-cables are the same thickness as those of the Brooklyn Bridge but considerably longer. If all the strands of steel wire which went into the making of the master cables were stretched to their extreme limits and placed end to end, they would extend from Mexico to Canada, following every indentation of the American coast.

410 U.S.A. The Golden Gate Bridge, San Francisco. The world's longest suspension bridge, with a span of 1,540 yds. ➤

After the ruin of modern war
men turn with courage to rebuild their cities from the rubble.

In the interval since the building of the Palais de Chaillot (see page 217) concrete has become an ever-more indispensable element in engineering and construction. To ensure greater speed and efficiency in its use, the concrete mixer was introduced, which could prepare the concrete at the exact place and time it was needed. This was invaluable, especially for work on 411 tunnels and dams★.

The Second World War had come, meanwhile, and proved that man's capabilities for construction were more than matched by his genius for destruction. Much of Europe was left in ruins. The abbey-shrine of Monte Cassino was destroyed by bombardment, and it was only one of innumerable cathedrals, palaces and monuments which were reduced to rubble. The liner *Normandie* went up in flames, and so did most of the centre of London; and British, German, French, Dutch and Belgian ports were bombed until nothing remained but heaps of debris. Much of European Russia was reduced to a wilderness of bare, scorched earth.

The war did, however, produce important construction works of a military nature: the Burma road, vast lines of fortifications, the development of Siberia as an industrial area, the building of the atomic city of Oakridge, Tennessee, and the elaborate organisation for the Normandy landings. Many of the features of the post-war world, too, such as atomic energy, rockets, radar and electronic engineering, had their origin, or their early development, in the military requirements of the war. There were also many developments on a smaller scale in techniques of building construction and methods which were to prove invaluable in the post-war work of reconstruction and modernisation.

No sooner was the war over than people set to work to rebuild. All over the world cities had to be rebuilt: London, Hamburg, Caen and Stalingrad, Tokyo and Hiroshima, to mention only a few. One of the most striking examples of reconstruction was to be seen in Warsaw. 412 Out of the heap of rubble★ which was all that remained of one of the loveliest quarters of the city the patient toil of the homeless inhabitants and the co-operation of numerous architects, artists and craftsmen recreated, stone by stone, 413 the glories of the past★. Around this enclave a new city was growing up.

412 Poland. Part of the centre of Warsaw after bombardment (1944).

413 The same district in 1960. The buildings have been reconstructed exactly as they were.

◄ 411 France. Mobile concrete mixer used in the construction of the Jouques Dam, Bouches-du-Rhone.

225

The French develop the valley
of the Rhône as the Americans that of the Tennessee.

414 France. Construction of a lock and power station at Donzère-Mondragon, Rhône Valley.

415 France. Aerial view of the Montélimar Lock and canal under construction.

In France the aftermath of the war left a great deal to be done. As well as repairing the damage and destruction of the war years there was also an urgent need to set French industry back on its feet; before this could be undertaken on an adequate scale the supply of electrical power, both for industrial and domestic consumption, had to be increased.

The 'Compagnie Nationale du Rhône', which had been formed before the war, prepared a scheme for exploiting the entire river basin and including, not only hydro-electricity but also irrigation and improved navigability. The first dam was opened at Génissiat in 1946. Next came the Donzère-Mondragon Dam (1952), incorporating the André-Blondel generating station* and one of the world's largest diversion canals, ten miles long and slightly broader than the Suez Canal. The construction of this canal and its locks* kept seven thousand men employed for four years. The conditions under which they worked were hard and often dangerous, particularly where they involved working under water in pressurised caissons or in the hundred and sixty foot-deep, three hundred-yard long tunnel carved out for the power station. With the use of loaders, like giant ploughs, a strip of earth almost a foot thick could be excavated at a rate of four miles an hour. The mechanical excavators used were capable of shifting eight cubic yards of rubble at a time, and there were marine drags that could move ten thousand tons of earth a day each.

The Serre-Ponçon dam, built in 1956, was constructed of earth on a concrete base six hundred and fifty yards thick. The purpose of the dam was to control the course of the River Durance*, an unpredictable river liable to sudden floods, to irrigate the southern foothills of the Alps and to produce an electricity supply of eight hundred million kilowatt-hours. The scheme involved moving a volume of earth equal to that of the great pyramid of Cheops, besides creating a reservoir covering an area of thirty-two thousand acres. This reservoir, which supplies badly-needed reserves of electricity for peak hours, is filled chiefly in the springtime from the melting Alpine snows. The underground generating station, vast as a cathedral, contains four turbo-alternators with a power of ninety thousand kilowatts each.

416 France. The empty bed of the river Durance, diverted during the construction of the Serre-Ponçon dam. ➤

The wealthiest towns of Germany
rise on a foundation of coal and iron.

417 Germany. The tallest building in the Federal Republic, at Düsseldorf. It has twenty-five floors.

418 Germany. Characteristic Ruhr landscape, on the outskir

The area of Westphalia between the Dortmund and the Rhine contains the greatest concentration of industry in the whole of western Europe. Düsseldorf, the wealthy capital of the region, contains the
417 tallest building in Germany*. Nearby, at the junction of the Rhine and the Ruhr, is the ancient Hanseatic town of Duisberg which has now become the largest port
418 in the world for river traffic*. The industrial area of the city covers well over two thousand acres and its dockyards extend for thirty miles. Here the seams of coal reach right under the docks: there are twelve million tons to be

Duisberg, the world's largest port for river traffic, showing barges and oil tankers on the Rhine.

extracted little by little in the course of maintenance work. Here coal is of primary importance. The extension of the navigable reaches of the Rhine, first from Mannheim to Strasbourg and then from Strasbourg as far as Basle, made it possible for coal from Westphalia to capture markets previously reserved for the Saar mines, and even to penetrate as far as Bavaria and compete with coal from Saxony. The industrial supremacy of the Ruhr was firmly established from the year 1881 as a result of the uses found for coke by-products and thanks to the development of the chemical industries and processes based on coal derivatives.

But the coal seams alone, though these are still estimated to contain some 65,000 million tons, and though the workings are highly mechanised, are not enough to ensure the continued industrial prosperity of the Ruhr except in conjunction with the steel industry. The origins of this industry go back to 1819 when Hartkort established his first machine shops at Wetter, on the River Ruhr. With the help of experts from England he soon expanded his interests to include everything from mines, blast furnaces, foundries, rolling mills to early railways and steam ships. This type of *Konzern*, or closely knit industrial unit, was to make a substantial contribution to the development of the Ruhr. Though anti-monopoly laws have to some extent forced the largest companies to split up their activities, the Krupps of Essen, who started from small beginnings two centuries ago, have managed to retain their empire. Krupps own collieries, iron-workings and shipyards; heavy industries all over the world use components of their manufacture, from trucks and locomotives to complete steel works and factories for chemicals and cement.

The Promised Land is reclaimed
from the desert by the toil of the Israeli communities.

419 Israel. Pioneers planting agaves in the Negev desert as part of a soil reclamation scheme.

421 View of the same field of agaves the following year. The reclamation scheme has been successful.

In 1948 a small nation became independent and immediately embarked on a programme of development which recalls some of the greatest undertakings of antiquity. Only this time the methods were the most up-to-date possible. The ancient land of Israel was re-born with a new population of the homeless and the dispossessed from all over the earth.

When the first Zionists arrived in 1908 to start work reclaiming land from the desert sands*, the biblical 'land flowing with milk and honey' was a wilderness where only thorn bushes grew and jackals roamed. Agriculture necessarily became a basic factor in the life of the Israeli state.

Beside the traditional type of village, comprising a number of small-holdings, new forms of land tenure grew up. Many of them were run as co-operatives of differing kinds*: nobody was paid wages and work was divided fairly among the members of the community. These rural societies were self-governing and responsible for their own defence, and the only law was absolute loyalty to the community. The multifarious schemes for land reclamation were planned as parts of a grand design; marshes had to be drained, arable land prepared for the plough, terraces built to prevent erosion, sandy areas consolidated, forests replanted and irrigation canals dug. Gradually, by these means, the land regained its old fertility*.

Afforestation altered both the soil and the climate. Since 1948 twenty million trees have been planted over an area of fifty thousand acres, while at the present time two hundred and fifty thousand acres—a twentieth of the total area of the country—have been irrigated.

The common danger threatening their frontiers has contributed much to keeping the communal spirit of the Israelis intact. One example of this among many is the *kibbutzim*, communities formed to undertake their own defence, farm their land in common and run factories to process their agriculture products. The first *kibbutz* was established in 1912, and today there are nearly three hundred. The population generally varies between one thousand and three thousand men, women and children who live together in a free association, with equal rights and obligations, administering their own society without wages or individual houses and with the minimum of personal possessions. In return for the work performed by each according to his capacities, the

420 Israel. Village based on family units and co-operative farming—not collective as in the *kibbutzim*.

kibbutz provides for each according to his needs, material and otherwise.

In the space of thirteen years the population of Israel has grown from six hundred thousand to over two million. In order to provide for this flow of immigrants it has become essential to reclaim the barren wastes of the Negev desert, which cover nearly half of the country.

The basis of this reclamation scheme has been the establishment of an immense
422 network of pipe-lines *, tunnels, reservoirs and canals in order to irrigate the desert by making the maximum use of available water supplies. A pipe-line running from north to south is to carry the Jordan waters to the Negev desert after crossing the length of the country and linking up with a number of secondary pipe-lines, thus forming the backbone of a nation-wide irrigation system.

In 1961 there were ninety settlements in the Negev, thirty of which were *kibbutzim*. Beersheba, the principal town at the northern end of the desert, now has a population of over twenty thousand. The Negev itself has more than ten thousand inhabitants, growing vegetables and fruit- and olive-trees. The ancient copper mines, which had been disused for two thousand years, are once again being worked to the full.

422 Israel. Laying a concrete irrigation pipe in the desert.

231

To be true to scale
public works in the African continent must be of vast extent.

423 Egypt. Construction of the Aswan Dam.

Nations with colonial territories in Africa had begun numerous large-scale construction programmes before their colonies achieved independence. The African states formed after independence took it upon themselves to complete the projects under construction and to launch out on even bolder schemes, for reasons of prestige as well as of practical necessity, but in many cases lacked the financial and technical resources to do so. One of the most important of these programmes, destined to bring prosperity to an under-developed area, is undoubtedly the Aswan Dam*. It is unfortunate, though, that when the dam is ready the temples of Abu Simbel (see page 30) and other important relics of antiquity will be swallowed up by the Nile; plans are being made, under the auspices of UNESCO, to save at least a part of the threatened buildings.

The new dam will consist of a rampart of granite about three miles in length and 1,375 yards thick and will contain the

greatest 'water bank' in the world: a lake three hundred and seventy-five miles long with a surface area of one thousand five hundred square miles. If the dam were to break, the force of water released would be sufficient to sweep away the whole of Upper Egypt with its five million inhabitants, to say nothing of a number of cities on the delta. But there is no danger of this happening as Aswan is a gravity-type dam, not a straightforward dyke; it locks up the current of the river, so to speak, and forces part of it to flow through the hydro-electric shafts and the rest by the diversion channel. This is the only example in the world of a reservoir capable of storing up the entire flow of a major river for a year and a half. The Aswan Dam is expected to increase the agricultural production of Egypt by 60% and to form the basis of a new industrial economy.

In North Africa many *wadis* have been dammed up* and their waters, which were formerly lost, used to irrigate farm-

424 The Cameroons. Road-rail bridge of pre-stressed concrete over the Wouri estuary at Douala.

The colonising powers show the way to exploit the mineral wealth of Africa.

lands and generate electricity. The storage dam erected at Bin-el-Ouidane in Morocco—the highest in Africa—supplies the country's two major hydro-electric stations. The Mellègue Dam in Tunisia holds the world record for the span of its arches. Many dams have also been built further south, in black Africa. In the Sounda gorge the Kouilou supplies energy to bauxite and aluminium industries, which are already proving a profitable source of income to some new republics, 426 such as Guinea*. Roads, ports and a highly developed system of communications are essential for the development of a continent as vast as Africa. The Gaya-Malanville bridge has encouraged a great increase in the ground-nut traffic between Niger and Dahomey. The bridges of Bamako and Abidjan have enabled these two towns to grow into great modern ports. The Douala bridge over 424 the Wouri estuary*, in the Cameroons, has been built in spite of the shifting mud of the river bed.

425 Algeria. The Iril Emda Dam. The largest area of reinforced concrete surface in the world—17½ acres.

426 Guinea. The Fria bauxite factory, a hundred miles inland, is Africa's biggest producer of aluminium.

In the Middle East dam builders
bring the hope of prosperity to barren regions.

427 Iran. The Sefi-Roud Dam under construction.

428 India. Construction work on a dam forming part of the Damodar Valley Scheme.

429 Iraq. Dokan Dam, built by the State Development Office

In the under-equipped nations great enterprises cannot be undertaken on the spur of the moment; here, just as in more advanced countries, these enterprises form part of multi-year development programmes, carefully organised and carried out by specially created official or state-sponsored organisations, who are often financed from outside.

Water control is even more important in Iraq and Iran than it is in Africa. Thousands of years ago Persian engineers were digging ingenious underground tunnels in order to tap deep-lying sources of water. Yet even though there are fifty

525,000 cubic metres of concrete were used in the construction of the dam.

thousand of these ganats, as they are called, the greater part of Persia is still desert. Projects such as the diversion of the Karoum into the desert basin, in which the only fertile spot is the oasis of
427 Shiraz, and the building of dams* to prevent the water dispersing uselessly into the sand, have become vital to Iran.

In the mining zone of Bengal in India the 'Damodar Valley Corporation', inspired by the T.V.A. in America (see page 220), has been in existence since 1948. A hundred and fifty million dollars
428 have been invested in a system of dams* and reservoirs. Factory towns and hydro-electric stations have grown up in the region, and the scheme serves to irrigate an agricultural valley three hundred and thirty miles long.

Quite the most remarkable of the major undertakings which are transforming the countries of the East into modern lands
429 is the Dokan Dam in Iraq,* sixty miles from Baghdad. In the little over three years the dam has taken to build, the engineers have fought a never-ending battle with a turbulent tributary of the Tigris called the Lesser Zab. Moreover, in order to prevent the torrid climate from impairing the reliability of the concrete structure a fantastically ingenious process was devised whereby an icing station diffused a constant flow of freezing cold water through a vast network of metal tubes which had been specially embedded in the work.

The engineers working on this project were mainly French, as they were on another scheme for blocking the Euphrates at Ramadi in order to divert flood waters into the great natural reservoir of Lake Habbaniyah. Here too there is hope that the land may one day regain its legendary appearance of an earthly paradise.

Moscow builds a palace
to higher education—the thirty-five storey university building . . .

430 Moscow. Work on the University Building.

431 The new university buildings: a 35-storey central tower flanked by 17-storey wings.

The new Moscow University building stands on a small hill overlooking the gilded domes of the city on the far side of the Moskva River. The old name for it was Sparrows Hill, but it has been rechristened after Lenin. The university 430 building*, which is one of the tallest in the Old World, was built between 1949 and 1953 as part of the fourth Five Year Plan (the 'plan of Victory and Reconstruction') launched by Stalin after the end of the war, and aimed at rebuilding Russia.

The building, dedicated to the scholar 431 Lomonosov, is thirty-five storeys high*

and occupies a site of a hundred and five acres. Facilities provided for the twenty-two thousand students include twelve faculties (journalism being one of them), three institutes, two hundred and ten lecture halls, two hundred and eighty-one laboratories, a hundred and sixty-three classrooms, three museums and the same number of observatories, a hospital and a large botanical garden. Lomonosov University, crowned by its 187-foot spire, is typical of the style of public buildings in Russia from the end of the war to the death of Stalin. The architectural design is gross and heavy-handed; the building

is overloaded with columns, statuary and decoration, everything being sacrificed to the taste for the colossal.

As the country's productivity recovered from the disruption caused by the German invasion, seventeen hundred devastated towns were rebuilt, as well as seventy thousand villages. At the same time there was the urgent problem of overcrowding in the towns. With the increase in industrialisation, the urban population had risen to sixty million within the space of thirty years. Living conditions were appalling. In Moscow as many as four families were living in

236

. . . and beside the Moskva River an area is set aside for sport and athletics.

432 Moscow. 115 ft. high ski-jump, opened in 1953. In the background is the Luniki sports stadium with accommodation for 100,000 spectators.

homes intended for one. Patiently the Russians set about transforming the capital into a modern city with broad, straight streets, granite embankments along the Moskva River and a growing number of tall apartment blocks in the new quarters of the city. These new residential blocks were built of huge slabs of prefabricated concrete, their weight only limited by the power of the cranes which had to lift them. Even domestic water-pipes and fittings were made all at once, installed in a single operation and connected to the mains. As a first step, factories for making prefabricated parts

were set up on the still vacant site of a new residential district.

432   The Russians compensated for the monotonous uniformity of these areas by creating ample parks nearby, with facilities for cultural and social activities and sports*. The great Luniki sports ground, which includes a stadium with room for over a hundred thousand spectators, two amphitheatres, four rinks and innumerable playing fields, was opened in 1956 on a loop of the Moskva River, facing Lenin Hill. The centrally situated Gorki Park of Rest and Culture covers nearly seven hundred and fifty

acres bordering on the Moskva. The Gorki Park is almost a garden city on its own, equipped with libraries, reading rooms, concert halls, theatres, arenas, gymnasia and swimming pools. A permanent agricultural exhibition, opened in 1954, was extended the following year to include industry. It now presents a complete picture of all aspects of the life and achievements of all the republics in the U.S.S.R. Surrounding the exhibition buildings are gardens containing something like five million flowers each year. In its first two years the Gorki Park received sixteen million visitors.

New waterways are
opened up across the steppes.

433 U.S.S.R. Volga-Don Canal. A convoy of logs bound for Tsimlank.

435 U.S.S.R. Construction of the 3,600,000 kw. power station at Bratsk on the

434 *Ibid*. Concrete-surfacing machine operated by one man; it can lay 1,800 sq. yds. a day.

The fifth Russian Five Year Plan (1951–1955) and the Seven Year Plan which succeeded it undertook the control of the Volga, the largest river in Europe.

A succession of lake-reservoirs, very deep, were formed to store up the spate of water which swelled the river in the spring for use in the dry season, and to prevent the disastrous floods which used to cause terrible damage to the surrounding land. These involved the building of dams, but huge locks were also built to give passage to the shipping and to the convoys of logs* which use the river. It is impossible to give a detailed description

A concrete wall across the Angara River creates an inland sea.

Angara River, Siberia. The reservoir formed by the dam is the largest artificial sea in the world, extending over an area of 2,200 sq. miles.

of this gigantic undertaking, but two of the more striking elements involved are worth a closer look.

One is the construction of the hydro-electric plant at Kuibyshev, the largest in the world with a yield of 11,000 million kilowatt-hours per year, which involved building a dam over three miles long. The most powerful new machines available were used on the work; they included the Piatiletka drag, which can shift a thousand cubic metres an hour, and machines able to line a canal-bed and its banks with an indestructible 434 surface*. Nineteen factories were kept

employed on this one scheme alone. ten of them on the manufacture of six million cubic metres of concrete, and five of them for stone crushing. Two towns grew up, one on each side of the river, to house the three hundred thousand workers: Jigulevsk and Komsomolsk. The reservoir formed by the dammed-up waters, covers nearly two thousand square miles. The other is Stalingrad power station, which uses another enor-mous dam to produce a further 11,000 million kilowatt-hours annually. As part of the same scheme the Volga, which flows southwards into the closed and

isolated Caspian Sea, was connected with the Don by means of a thirteen-lock canal.

But it is in the newly developed lands of Siberia that the Russians have been con-centrating their greatest efforts. An 435 electric plant built at Bratsk* was to break all previous records. It uses the energy of the Angara River, whose waters pour out of Lake Baikal in a swift-moving current that never freezes over for the first six miles of its course. A concrete wall four hundred and twenty feet high contains an inland 'sea' three hundred and seventy miles long by twenty five broad.

As new power stations are built
Russia's industries gather momentum.

436 U.S.S.R. Factory for the manufacture of artificial fibres, opened in 1959 under the Seven Year Plan to develop national economy.

There is another dam on the Angara, between the sea of Bratsk and Lake Baikal, at the ancient city of Irkutsk. It was built to supply energy for a three hundred-mile long coal-mining basin, with an output equalling that of the whole of France, and the work went forward under almost unbelievably difficult conditions. It snows there sixty-one days in the year and the temperature is 30° below zero for months at a time. The town of Irkutsk, founded in 1658 to force the Buryat tribes to pay their tribute of furs, is now approaching a million inhabitants.

In 1958 the Soviet Union had raised her electricity supply to 1,120 kilowatts per person, compared with an average of 4,160 in the U.S.A., 2,180 in the British Isles and 1,400 in France. But the Seven Year Plan aims to raise this to 2,300 437 kilowatts by 1965. At Kharkov*, and also at Leningrad, technicians are working

to double and even treble the electricity supply and to install a new 124,000-mile network of power cables.

However, it is still in Siberia that the greatest strides forward are being made. There are to be other giant dams besides the one at Bratsk, in central Siberia. Electric turbines at Krasnoyarsk, on the three thousand-mile Yenisei River, of which the Angara is only a tributary, are to produce 15,000 million kilowatt-hours a year. Earth has been excavated from the site at a rate of a thousand lorry loads a day by the thirty thousand workers, and a complete new town, Volgski, has been built to accommodate them. Kras-436 noyarsk* already possesses the largest artificial fibres factory anywhere in the Old World. Out of an estimated hundred and ten extensive iron-smelting works in the U.S.S.R., fifty-two are in the Urals, the Kuzbass or the Far East of the Union, and several are giant combines. The

population of Siberia has increased ten-fold in the last twenty years. Until the last war Novosibirsk, two thousand miles from Moscow, seemed to most Russians like the end of the world. Now, from a simple workers' camp set up in 1895 while work was in progress on the Trans-Siberian railway, it has grown into a town of over a million and a half inhabitants. As well as lying on the Trans-Siberian railway, Novosibirsk is also the termi-nus for the 'Turksib' line. During the Second World War it became a vast grain storage centre, taking the place of the occupied Ukraine. Seventy air-craft and heavy engineering works have opened up there, and the region benefits from the coal reserves of nearby Kuzbass, amounting to some 400,000 million tons. A vast scientific research centre has grown up on the outskirts of Novosibirsk, consisting of twelve research institutes with a staff of about four thousand.

437 U.S.S.R. Kharkov. Plant making electrical components.

In China, where labour is plentiful, mechanisation develops more slowly than in the West.

With the exception of the Summer Palace, near Pekin, and the modernisation of her main sea ports, China has till recently contributed little to the great works of mankind since the Ming dynasty (see page 115). Now she is stirring again and the Chinese in their millions are toiling to turn their backward nation into a modern, industrial power. In order to protect the city of Pekin from the floods which have menaced it for centuries past, a huge reservoir has had to be built, sufficiently large to supply water to irrigate the entire province. Labourers travel immense distances to work on the reservoir, and, in the absence of trucks, the earth has to be carted by tireless columns of men on foot. Each man carries two baskets slung on a bamboo pole over his shoulder; he tips their contents onto the dam and then turns back and repeats the process, over and over again, often for twelve hours a day★★. It is the same where any major building programme is going on.

In 1948 the victorious Communist revolutionary government found the country in a desperate economic plight, totally out of step with the modern world and ravaged by the endemic plagues of flood and drought and terrible famines. They were faced with the problem of transforming these millions of peasants into a workable, technological civilisation. Marxist ideology, disseminated among the peasants by Party Officials, played the same role in the building of the new China as fear of the lash did in the building of Babylon, or the inspiration of faith did in the raising of medieval cathedrals. Between 70% and 90% of the population were mobilised, and these great reserves of human labour, prepared to give up all claims to personal freedom and work as and where they were directed, made possible the most radical programme of planned reform known to history. From a strictly segregated class system, the Chinese were suddenly and brutally pitchforked into a most extreme form of social revolution, and the lives of countless millions of people changed completely,

whether they liked it or not. The state set in motion a long-term plan on an unprecedented scale. Not even the Russians had conceived of anything of such magnitude as the Fifty Year Plan which was intended to transform China from a backward and underdeveloped nation into a major power. The Fifty Year Plan was really to consist of a related series of ten year plans, the first of which was entirely concerned with the development of Manchuria. But even at this early stage plans were already in operation to decide the sites and capacities of vast factory areas in Honan and Hopeh, the colossal hydro-electric plants on the Yellow River and the Blue River, and the creation of a 'Chinese Essen' at Pao-tow, as well as a 'Chinese Baku' at Yumen and a 'Chinese Magnitogorsk' to be built by a Sino-Soviet condominium for the exploitation of Sin-kiang. Altogether a hundred and fifty-six major projects were scattered throughout the immense territory stretching from the Mongolian frontiers to Tibet and the Kirghiz Republic.

438
439

438–439 China. Pekin region. 50,000 workers were employed building the dam for the reservoir in the valley of the thirteen Ming tombs.

Willing hands, makeshift tools and a common impulse contribute to the makings of the new China.

440 China. Student volunteers dredging a river bed.

441 China. Mechanical hoist operated by a treadmill—as used in medieval Europe.

In the new China, as in Siberia, much of the people's energy is concentrated on building dams. The half-naked workers in 440 the picture*, clearing a river bed by means of a human chain, are students from Pekin University who voluntarily give up part of their time to the state. In more remote parts of the country peasants can be seen drawing water with a treadmill in a way that has scarcely 441 changed since the Middle Ages*. War has been declared on the four great rivers which have tyrannised the Chinese people from time immemorial: the Hwang Ho, or Yellow River, the Howei, the Han and

the Yangtse. The Yellow River, the uncontrollable 'curse of the sons of Han', has burst its banks fifteen hundred times in three thousand years, often killing tens of thousands of people and leaving millions homeless. The Chinese aim to prevent the repetition of such disasters and at the same time to promote their country to the front rank of the world's industrial nations. The development scheme for the lower Yellow River covers a surface area greater than that of the whole of France: a region very rich in coal, iron and rare metals, which supports a population of some 150 million. The 1955 plan pro-

442 vides for the building of forty-six dams* and twenty-four reservoirs in ten years. Three million men are employed to build a dam three hundred and twenty feet high on a loop of the San-Men River, creating a reservoir covering nine hundred square miles. Human labour is being 443 supplemented by mechanical tools*— bull-dozers, excavators, cranes and trucks —as fast as the factories can turn them out. When the San-Men power station reaches its full capacity of a million kilowatts the scheme will be extended to permit three million acres of land to be brought under cultivation.

442 China. Conveyor belts and traditional methods used simultaneously to clear debris from a building site.

443 China. Pneumatic drills and metal crowbars in use at the same time during the construction of a dam on the Yellow River.

The road to industrialisation in China is long and fraught with difficulties. The steel works of An Shan are a foretaste of success.

444 China. Home-made steel foundry at Shin Shin.

Innumerable slogans help to stimulate China's great leap forward. Politicians proclaim: 'We shall conquer nature. We shall defy her and she shall yield.' 'Man can achieve everything.' 'The great works of the masses shall be numberless as the stars in the evening sky.' The boldest step of all was the transformation of rural into industrial communities. At a single stroke, five hundred million peasants were turned into a conscious and organised proletariat. Where factories did not exist they had to be built. The Chinese countryside, which in 1945 was still living in the Middle Ages, suddenly moved without any intermediate steps right into the Machine Age. Each commune was responsible for its own industrial development, however rough the means. Steel manufacture was at the top of the agenda and improvised blast furnaces*, built by the villagers out of whatever came to hand, sprang up in their thousands all over the country side, a symbol of the new China. To obtain the raw materials for the village steelworks, people were forced to hunt for serviceable scrap metal wherever they could*. But at least there was no lack of enthusiasm.

Not all the blast furnaces, however, were improvised. Those dominating the city of An Shan*, the greatest iron-smelting centre of the country, show up for miles as a landmark to anyone crossing Manchuria. This great industrial belt, where seams of coal and iron-ore are to be found a bare forty miles apart, was first developed on a large scale by the Japanese invaders between 1917 and 1945. When they left they destroyed all they could, but the Chinese set about the task of rebuilding An Shan with amazing speed.

Now steel production goes up by more than a million tons a year and amounts to over half the total for the whole of China—or the equivalent of half the total production of Germany, two-thirds that of France, though only one tenth that of the United States.

445 China. Steel production at Tsohsien. Peasants raking over ashes for scrap.

446 China. Steel mills at An Shan. ➤

Prosperous South American capitals show the way to urban modernisation.

447 Venezuela. View of the capital, Caracas, showing the Simon Bolivar centre with main roads running underneath it.

Before 1950 the only way to reach Caracas, the capital of Venezuela, from its sea port of La Guaira—a distance of some six miles as the crow flies—involved an arduous drive along twenty miles of mountain road which took an hour to negotiate because of its three hundred and sixty bends. Now the La Guaira-Caracas motorway has reduced the journey to ten miles and made it possible to cross the difficult country lying between the sea and the city at top speeds. The new road has broad dual carriageways, ventilated tunnels and three giant bridges, one of which is supported

by the biggest concrete arch ever built in the continent of America. At the entrance to Caracas the road crosses another bridge, of pre-stressed concrete, before linking up with the network of broad, open streets which run between ultra-modern buildings, dominated by the 447 skyscraper of the Simon Bolivar centre★.

With the vast wealth accruing from her oilfields Venezuela has in fact set out to break records. There is, for instance, the Merida cable-car; each car is pressurised and carries forty passengers to the top of one of the highest peaks in the Sierra Nevada. Built in the amazingly

short space of fourteen months, the cable-way covers a distance of eight miles, reaches a height of 15,800 feet and has the world's longest span of cable between two pylons: 3,300 yards.

Venezuela is not the only place in South America to lead the way in modernisation. There are many other examples. In 1958 French and Peruvian technicians succeeded in laying the highest electric power cable in the world, along twenty miles of almost perpendicular peaks of the Andes. Tons of cement, water and steel girders had to be carried by mule, and sometimes even on the

Prefabrication solves many problems of construction: buildings, bridges, now tunnels adopt this method.

448 Cuba. Havana. One of the 16,000-ton, 50-yd. long prefabricated sections of the submarine tunnel.

backs of men, up to heights of anything between thirteen hundred and sixteen hundred feet in order to erect the hundred pylons which were to carry the cable.

An even more remarkable example of South American ingenuity is the Havana road tunnel, opened in 1958. The capital of Cuba already stretched for ten miles along the western shore of its bay and desperately needed to expand. But in order to exploit the thousands of acres of excellent land awaiting development on the eastern shore there had to be some means of crossing the nine hundred yards of sea dividing the two sides. A bridge

would obstruct one of the busiest harbours in the world, and there could be no question of this, even if only while its contruction was in progress. The sea bed, largely composed of sand and coral, presented insurmountable obstacles to boring a tunnel. Finally the engineers conceived the idea of dredging a deep trench right across the bay and laying in this five prefabricated concrete sections of a tunnel which could then be joined together to form a single unit, stretching from one side to the other. To do this 448 they built floating sections* which could be sunk at exactly the desired spot when

the time came. The same principle was used by the Allies for building the famous 'mulberry' harbour off the Normandy beachheads in June 1944, though the 'mulberries' weighed no more than seven thousand tons each, while those used at Havana weighed as much as sixteen thousand. The operation was carried out with such precision that the sections were sunk into the trench prepared for thcm with scarcely perceptible gaps between each one. All that remained was to seal the joints with concrete and to remove the watertight bulkheads; the result was the world's largest prefabricated tunnel.

The Ruhr? The Mersey?
No—heavy industry in the land of the flowering cherry.

449 Japan. The port of Yawata, Kyushu—centre of the steel industry, and located near submarine coal seams.

449 The Japanese port of Yawata* has once again become the chief centre of the steel industry in the whole of Asia. Its redevelopment is typical of the fantastic impetus behind Japan's industrial and commercial revival, and makes an interesting contrast between Communist China's 'great leap forward' and the capitalist, free-enterprise economy of Japan. Two factors contributing to this revival have been the particular character of Japanese society and the substantial aid from the United States. An example of the lengths to which this aid has gone is the building of the Sakuma dam. The American firm responsible for the undertaking repeated

almost exactly the gravity-dam being built at Pine Flat in California. Not only were the same plans and drawings used for both Pine Flat and Sakuma but Sakuma was also constructed with the very same equipment and diversion channels as had been used at Pine Flat.

As for the first factor, the character of Japanese society, this was shown chiefly in the importance of the ancient family trusts, called *zaibatsus*, which reappeared in spite of the severe legal measures of 1945. Since 1952 the Fuji steelworks have been producing a quarter of Japan's total steel output and half her cast iron. Today half the mills are owned by ten major

cotton firms. Seventy per cent of the iron and steel is produced by seven companies. Five companies produce ninety per cent of the country's copper. The three *zaibatsus*, Mitsui, Mitsubishi and Sumitomo, control forty-five per cent of coal production. At the top of these huge pyramids stands the 'holding company', the mother company which holds the smaller associates on behalf of the members of a single family. In the case of the Mitsubishi trust, for example, this is the Iwasaki family. Since 1958, the Mitsubishi trust has taken the lead in shipbuilding, and it owns the entire centre of Tokyo, the largest city in the world.

Oak Ridge
and Vostok

from
the atom
to the cosmos

The new alchemists
turn base metals into alloys.

450 Japan. Copper refinery at Shisakagima. An important modern use of copper is in the manufacture of electricity wires.

450 The last chapter of this history of the great works of mankind opens with a picture of a copper refinery*. Without the copper wire which carries power and light over thousands of miles none of the great hydro-electric schemes described in the previous chapter would have been of any use. None of the other marvels of this latter half of the Twentieth Century would be possible without metals capable of withstanding the extremes of heat and pressure—as great as those encountered by space rockets.

This century has seen a momentous development in things great and small, from the journeys of the astronauts to the splitting of the atom. A few decades ago man was an earthbound traveller; now he is exploring outer space. The splitting of the atom has released fantastic sources of energy which man has not yet learned to control. But neither atomic power nor space travel would have been conceivable without the continual improvement in techniques for the fusion of metals.

As early as 1900 tools were being exhibited made of steel alloyed with tungsten and chrome and capable of working to very high speeds—high enough to produce red-hot shavings—without losing their edge. As the motor industry developed it started an increasing demand for alloys that could resist shock and wear. Today the Boeing 707 airliner, the atomic vessels *Nautilus* and *Lenin*, the Jodrell Bank radiotelescope, the Mercury capsule, Gagarin's *Vostock* or Glenn's *Friendship II* have been feasible by virtue of the existence of special alloys with precisely calculated mechanical, physical and chemical properties. They must be extra-light, extra-durable and capable of resisting extremely high temperatures before melting. The development of more and more complicated machines involves the use of rare metals or of special steels incorporating nickel, chrome, cobalt, tungsten, or vanadium.

451 U.S.S.R. Manganese mines at Tchiatouri, Georgia. This metal is increasingly used in the manufacture of hard-wearing, shock-proof alloys.

The coal industry, which was once concerned merely with mining, now involves a whole series of related processes such as the manufacture of coke and its various by-products. None the less coal no longer enjoys the virtual monopoly as a source of power which it held in the Nineteenth Century. Oil, hydro-electricity and, now, atomic power have all appeared to threaten its supremacy.

Coal has lost its lead in the field of mining as well. Nowadays new mines are opening at a faster rate than ever, but they are concerned with different pro-

451 ducts. Cobalt, uranium, manganese*, bauxite, as well as the oldest metals known to man: copper, tin and lead are much more sought after than coal.

But whether they are extracting coal or more precious minerals, a whole new range of machines and tools have become available which can increase production and also make their work less laborious for the men on the job. Miners now wear
452 standard clothes* and equipment which offer the maximum of safety and comfort for their work. The old pick and shovel have been replaced by mechanical drills.

Electric cutters are able to get through anything between a hundred and fifty and three hundred and fifty tons a day, and there are machines which not only cut the coal but can load and carry it as well. Fast planes, like ploughs, can move along the coal face at a rate of sixteen inches a second, cutting away chips up to four inches thick. In some places where non-ferrous metals are being mined it is even possible to work with bulldozers, and excavating machines are used to take the place of hundreds of workers. In Kentucky, U.S.A., the 'River Queen', a

are systematically exploited.

453 Canada. Power drills in use in a copper mine.

452 France. Miners' changing rooms at Merlebach, Moselle.

mechanical shovel weighing 1,700 tons (or as much as two hundred trucks), does the work of fifty thousand labourers. Mine galleries can be opened up by auto-

453 matic boring machines*: electrically operated dredging machines are capable of excavating 3,500 tons in eight hours— giving a new lease of life to open cast

454 mining*. The largest open cast mine in Europe, at Fortuna-Nord, near Cologne, possesses a 5,600-ton caterpillar excavator as tall as a sixteen-storey building which can eat into the hillside at the rate of nearly three million bushels a day.

454 Australia. Mechanical dredge in an open-cast mine at Yallourn, Victoria.

The atom is split, a new industry founded
which mobilises vast resources of technological skill.

On July 16th, 1945, at five o'clock in the morning, the first atomic bomb was exploded in the desert of New Mexico. On August 6th 1945, Hiroshima was destroyed and eighty thousand of its inhabitants killed by a single bomb. Yet the discovery and use of atomic energy is an irrevocable step in the development of man's knowledge; as every page of this history has shown, man has always been bent on refashioning nature according to his own uses.

Although scientists had been working on the subject for fifty years, it was not until the eve of World War II that they finally made the discoveries which opened the way to the full development of atomic energy. Scientists of many countries— Englishmen and Germans, Frenchmen and Italians, Americans and many European refugees who had fled to the U.S.— contributed to discovering the secret of the atom. In the summer of 1940 the entire world stock of heavy water, 175 kilogrammes, which was indispensable to the research work and was produced in

456 Norway*, was saved from the Germans. England, however, was in grave danger at the time, and had to leave the most intensive research to the United States. By December 1942 the first experimental pile (uranium-graphite) was set in operation at Chicago University. It was now known that the fission of the atomic nucleus of uranium 235 could produce a chain reaction and release an enormous concentration of energy. Never yet had man come close to releasing pent-up energy on this scale; never had any experiment obtained such dizzying results. The energy produced by the annihilation of a fraction of a nuclear combustible is six million times greater than that resulting from the combustion of the same quantity of coal.

To obtain uranium 235, it had first to be separated from its twin substance, uranium 238, with which it is naturally linked. For this purpose a gigantic atomic plant was built at Oak Ridge, Tennessee, where there was an ample supply of water and electricity provided by the

great ressources of the T.V.A. (see p. 220).

The buildings for this factory are a mile and a quarter long, six hundred and sixty yards broad and as tall as a four-storey 455 building*. Another factory was built for a second method consisting of a hundred and seventy separate buildings. Here a number of electro-magnets were made, containing enough iron to build a whole fleet of battleships; in the absence of sufficient copper, fourteen thousand tons of silver from the Federal Reserve Bank had to be melted down to make electric wires.

Since the end of the war the great powers have not slackened their research into the possibilities of atomic energy. Under the stimulus of the cold war and the need for a new source of industrial power in a changing world new and increasingly complex laboratories and 457 testing stations* are slowly widening our knowledge of the principles underlying atomic energy. In Britain, the atomic power station at Calder Hall has been in 458 operation since 1956*.

455 U.S.A. Oak Ridge, Tennessee. Factory for the manufacture of uranium 235 by means of diffusion of gases. The main building is 1¼ miles long.

456 Norway. Heavy-water factory which in 1940 held the entire world stock.

457 France. Three million-volt generator in a laboratory at Ivry.

458 Great Britain. Site of the Berkeley atomic power station, on the Severn, during erection of the world's largest pressurised caisson, made of steel.

The nuclear physicist reduces matter
to its basic elements and unleashes a power he can ill control.

The principle on which an atomic reactor works is basically simple. It involves the breaking down of uranium by a carefully controlled process. The core of a reactor, such as the one built by the Atomic Energy Authority at Calder Hall, consists of a mass of graphite moderator into which fuel rods and control rods are inserted from above. This core is housed in a pressurised vessel of aluminium or magnesium. The neutrons thrown off by the fission of uranium nuclei are slowed down by the graphite, with the result that they can be captured by the uranium, provoking the chain reaction which produces heat that can be transformed into energy. Many different types of reactor have already been designed. It is also possible to use plutonium, produced from uranium 238, with graphite, heavy water, beryllium or other substances as a moderator to slow down the neutrons, and a coolant of carbon gas, heavy water or liquid metal. There are even some small reactors, known as 'swimming-pool reactors'* in which ordinary water can be

459

usefully and economically used as a coolant.

Today there are experimental stations for the development of the uses of atomic energy* in many countries. The United States*, Russia and, since 1954, France have all developed either experimental or normal-service nuclear power stations and the United Kingdom has embarked on a large-scale system of nuclear power stations. Seven are under construction for the Central Electricity Authority.

461

Other European nations have pooled their research and resources, either through Euratom or some larger organisation, and in this way Norway, Germany*, Belgium, Italy and Holland have been able to make considerable advances in the field of nuclear research.

462

The building of a nuclear reactor, whether for a power station or for experimental purposes, entails constructions whose scale are out of all proportion to the infinitely microscopic particles at the heart of the work. The shielding walls of an atomic pile may easily contain fifty thousand tons of concrete. Research into

the nature and behaviour of nuclear explosions demands equally elaborate preparations. The artificial creation of cosmic rays produced by the bombardment of atomic particles is carried out with the help of various types of 'accelerators'. The huge Russian synchro-cyclotron at Dubno* has been surpassed by the synchrotron built by C.E.R.N. (the European Centre for Nuclear Research) at Meyrin, near Geneva. This is six hundred and fifty feet in diameter and contains a hundred electro-magnets, each one weighing close on four hundred tons. In this, protons are accelerated to a speed of 185,000 miles per second. The Americans, at Brookhaven, and the Russians have even more powerful instruments to work with.

460

The effects of atomic radiation can be studied without actually letting off bombs by means of a small reactor which can be raised or lowered at will to release a belt of neutrons. The tower in the Nevada desert which is to be used for this experiment is to be fifteen hundred feet high.

459 U.S.A. Inside a reactor at Oak Ridge.

460 U.S.S.R. Synchro-cyclotron at the nuclear research institute at Dubno, Moscow.

461 U.S.A. Assembling an atomic reactor at Dresden, Tennessee.

462 Germany. Dome of the atomic research centre at Munich.

Electro-magnets, arranged in a ring, guide the course of protons as they speed round.

257

Atomic energy can drive sea-craft through, and beneath, the Polar ice.

463 U.S.S.R. The atomic ice-breaker *Lenin*.

465 The calorific energy produced in the reactor of a nuclear power station* can be turned into mechanical energy in order to work turbines and produce electricity. On the same principle it can also be used as a substitute for fuel oil to supply power to marine engines. A start has indeed been made in this field.

463 In 1957 the U.S.S.R. launched the atomic ice-breaker, *Lenin**, and she made her maiden voyage in 1959. The *Lenin* is powered by three water reactors fuelled by enriched uranium, and is capable of sailing for a year without refuelling. A few dozen kilogrammes of uranium are sufficient for the entire voyage. The ship carries passengers and freight as well as opening up a passage through the Arctic ice for ships in her wake. This makes polar navigation possible all year round.

464 The American nuclear submarine *Nautilus**, built chiefly through the efforts of Admiral Rickover, opened a new era in naval history in August 1958 when she remained submerged for the whole of the eight thousand-mile journey from Honolulu to Iceland under the North Pole. The *Nautilus* travelled at an average depth of five hundred feet, and eighteen hundred miles of her journey were actually underneath the polar ice. In both these ships, as in America's first atomic cargo ship, the heat released by the reactors is extracted by a fluid and turned into mechanical energy in a turbine.

Today we have atomic submarines. Tomorrow there may be long-distance atomic railways and planes. Like every other aspect of atomic power, nuclear-powered engines are as yet only in their infancy. But scientists are already looking beyond the fission of heavy atoms to the fusion of light atoms such as hydrogen. The fission reaction is tens of thousands of times more powerful and its raw material can be found in quantity anywhere on earth. The possibilities are there, and time will show how they can best be used.

464 U.S.A. The atomic submarine *Nautilus* entering New York harbour after her voyage under the Arctic Circle.

465 France. The G 2 Reactor at Marcoule, Gard. ➤

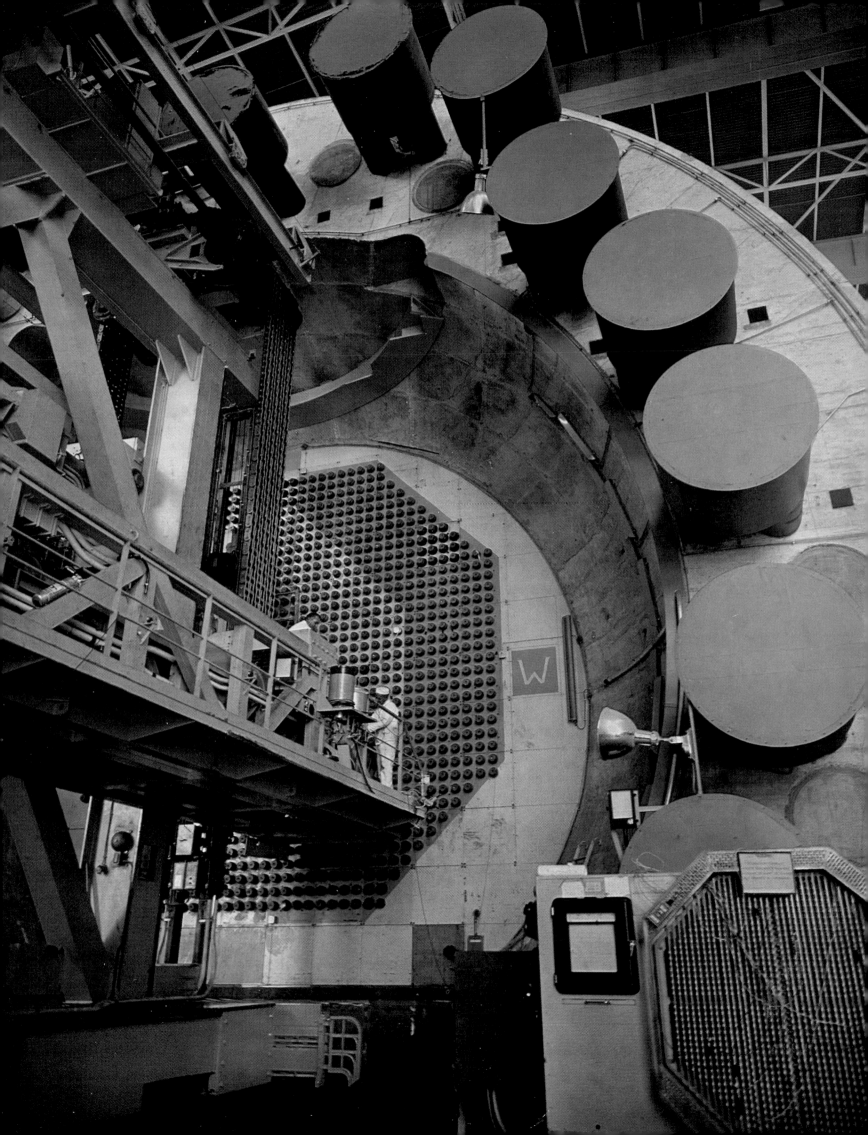

Oil is sought wherever it can be found,
even at sea; once it is refined it has a million uses.

Since the 'oil rushes' of the Nineteenth Century (see page 194) petroleum companies have sent prospectors to every corner of the world. In less than half a century oil has become a staple material of our modern civilisation. While the chemical properties of oil are explored by scientists in the refineries—eerie, 466 metallic piles such as this*—geophysicists develop new methods of prospecting for oil far below the earth's surface by means of magnetism, shock waves and the like. Undersea prospecting, first attempted in the Louisiana marshes, has resulted in the erection of oil derricks 467 actually in the water*. Diamond-tipped rotary drills are a great improvement on the earlier percussion type for boring.

It was the discovery of the Kirkuk oil-field in Iraq that revived the prospectors' interest in the Middle East. The first Saudi Arabian oil came on the market in 1939. In 1946 the peninsular of Qatar 468 and the small islands of Bahrein* in the Persian Gulf at last began producing oil in immense quantity, justifying the hopes which had led people to prospect there since 1940. The richest yield in the whole world started coming from the tiny sheikdom of Kuwait, also on the Persian Gulf. And in 1960 oil wells in the Sahara went into production.

The laying of pipe-lines across mountains and valleys, beneath rivers and even under the sea has opened up equally important fields of enterprise. Ever since the great pipe-line was laid between Baku and the Black Sea port of Batum in 1896, this method of oil transport has been constantly improved. Pipe-lines run from Kirkuk to Tripoli and to Haifa, and, more recently still, there is the Tapline from the Persian Gulf to the Mediterranean— eleven hundred miles of it, containing more steel than thirty-six Eiffel Towers put together. By 1957 there were 167,000 miles of crude oil pipe-line in the world as well as 38,000 miles for refinery products and 510,000 for natural gas.

Today the main centres of the oil industry are those where the crude oil is refined and broken down into components for the manufacture of numerous by-products, such as butyl (synthetic rubber), detergents, solvents, and plastics of every kind. Oil is reputed to be the basic ingredient for eighty thousand by-products, employed in the manufacture of five hundred thousand different articles for use in all spheres of human activity.

467 Venezuela. Oil derricks dotting Lake Maracaïbo.

468 Bahrein. The oil refinery also receives crude oil by underwater pipeline from the Arabian oil-fields.

466 U.S.A. Lighting effects inside an oil refinery at Bayonne, New Jersey.

On the production lines
in the car factories each worker is a specialist.

469 France. 'Dauphines' on an assembly line in the Renault factory at Flins.

470 U.S.A. Machine shop at the Ford factory, Detroit.

It is the motor industry that has done the most to develop one of the principal aids to modern industry: the factory assembly line*. The assembly line appeared for the first time in the United States around 1890. The opening up of the West by the pioneers had given an enormous boost to grain production in America, but the railway companies were still short of working capital and therefore were compelled to wait and see what the forecasts were for the harvest before arranging for transport. This meant building additional rolling stock at the last minute, to carry the grain. To do this they installed six parallel lines in their workshops: four used to assemble the wheels, axles and lastly the waggons, and the other two to bring the parts needed on the job. The assembly teams moved from one waggon to the next as the work progressed. The next step was to leave the workers at their posts and move each waggon up the line as it reached a new stage of completion. As a result the work was speeded up and the workers on each particular stage of the job became specialists at their own task. Moreover, when the men were not continually moving around, a far greater number could work in the same place without getting in each other's way. Each waggon moved up one place every forty-five minutes, and it took seven hours from the time the wheels were assembled to the final emergence of the completed waggon ready for painting.

This development was taken a stage further by the huge Chicago slaughterhouses with the introduction of overhead conveyors to eliminate handling of the meat. In building the first American motor factory*, Henry Ford adopted both these methods: the assembly line system for the car chassis, and the overhead conveyor belt system for other parts.

Today the Wolfsburg factories in Germany contain 56 miles of overhead conveyor belts in their 870,000 square yards of buildings. Automation has led to a further extension of the chain principle: sixteen machines can transform a block of steel into an engine, by means of eight hundred different operations, without its once being touched by human hand. Today automobile factories are becoming staffed increasingly by experts*, and the leading car manufacturers, who as often as not produced their prototypes in a backyard shed, have now taken over huge areas for their plants*.

471 U.S.A. Ford factory, Detroit. Car parks for employees' cars.

472 U.S.A. Detroit. Ford technicians with the prototype of the 'Falcon' compact model.

**As the volume of traffic rises
the road system must be revised.**

473 U.S.A. Cloverleaf intersection, aimed at speeding the traffic at the approaches to a large city.

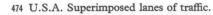
474 U.S.A. Superimposed lanes of traffic.

If the railways took the carriage trade away from the roads, the growth of the motor industry soon re-established the importance of road communications; indeed, as the new cars started to roll off the assembly lines in their thousands, an adequate road system became a vital necessity in all highly developed countries. Today the civil engineer is faced with a transport problem which would never have been imagined in the days of the coach and four.

The motorway is becoming a familiar sight all over Europe and America. Its basic principles are to ensure a free flow of traffic by imposing restrictions on parking, by providing lay-bys and clear-ways, and by building a carefully devised system of bridges and junctions to 473 eliminate crossroads*; in order to avoid the risk of frontal collisions, dual carriage-474 ways and fly-overs* are provided. By these means it is possible in some measure to reduce accident rates. The American definition of the ideal motorway is a road with 'built-in safety'.

Up to the present time the United States possesses a 20,000 mile network of motorways ('parkways' or 'turnpikes'), and this figure will shortly be trebled by the addition of a further 40,000 miles. A number of these motorways recall the

475 France. Road junction outside Orly airport, near Paris. North-south traffic passes under the airport building and the runways.

early days of the New York elevated railway: built on the outskirts of great cities, the 'skyways' are in actual fact viaducts striding over the buildings. That running from Newark to Jersey City is the longest in the world.

In Europe the need for new highways was realised more slowly and available financial resources were often diverted to the more urgent business of rebuilding cities and railways. But since 1955 all modernisation and development plans have included the construction of motorways as a major undertaking.

In France this effort can be seen in the 475 new road junction at Orly*, near Paris, opened in 1961, which takes the main road from Paris to the south right underneath the main runways of the airport. Other countries, too, have not lagged behind in road construction. The M.1 from London to the Midlands, the Salzburg-Vienna road, the Lübeck–Hamburg–Frankfurt–Basle network, and the autostrada from Milan to Naples are all built for a great volume of fast traffic. Russia, after building the Moscow–Minsk highroad, has turned her attention to one from Moscow to Pekin—the longest motorway in the world.

In all these projects the chief material used is concrete, but valuable use is also being made of new discoveries in the field of soil chemistry and synthetic surfaces. It is important that the road surface should be able to stand up to sudden braking, acceleration and skidding from heavy traffic without showing rapid signs of wear. Thanks to machines which can surface six miles of road per day, road building can proceed at an exceptional pace.

Progress is being made at such a rate that already it is not pure fantasy to dream of roads running from Glasgow to Vladivostock. In America the Panamerican Highway already links Alaska with Central America.

Is the Dover packet an anachronism? A road or rail link between England and the Continent is no longer impracticable.

However, there can be no question of roads running from Britain across Europe while the English Channel continues to provide an effective barrier. Projects are now being re-appraised which were dismissed as fantastic a hundred years 476 ago*. The partisans are divided between a tunnel and a bridge. If a bridge, it would be far and away the largest in the world: twenty-two miles long and a clear two hundred and thirty feet above sea level. Those in favour of a bridge point with triumph to the bridge over the Seine at Tancarville, the longest in Europe, which has supporting piers as high as the Arc de Triomphe and which gives a sufficient indication of the capabilities of modern civil engineering. The advocates for the bridge also argue that a road-tunnel would be impossible to ventilate adequately. Even supposing it were possible to keep the air fresh, there would still be the problem of fatigue resulting from a long drive in a tunnel. But the 477 tunnel's partisans object that the cost of a fully equipped bridge carrying nine lanes of road and rail traffic must be prohibitive compared with the traditional plan for a rail tunnel. This plan consists simply of dual tunnels, one for each direction, each twenty-three feet in diameter. Double-decker trains passing through the tunnel every ten minutes would be able to carry eighteen hundred cars per hour. Moreover two test tunnels have already been dug, one from the French and one from the English side; they were cut in 1880, in record time, with the help of Brunton's machine*, an outsize drill specially designed for cutting through soft rock. With today's machines, capable of piercing the granite of Mont Blanc at a rate of thirteen yards a day, almost anything seems possible.

But if the Channel link has still not left

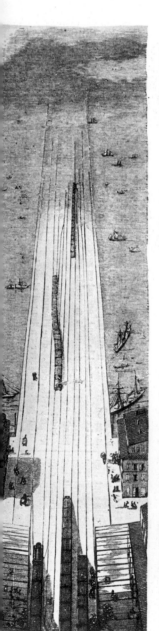

476 Projected designs for a Channel Bridge which would not cause interference to shipping, as published in a French magazine of 1867.

Another tunnel is bored through the Alps, this time to carry road traffic.

the drawing-board stage, a road tunnel 478 through Mont Blanc* is already in the course of construction. When completed the tunnel will cut the road distance from the French valley of Chamonix to the Italian Val d'Aosta down to seven miles. The bulk of the rock extracted from the tunnel is being used to make the approach roads as well as to surface the walls of what will be the longest road tunnel in the world. The motorist using the Mont Blanc tunnel will scarcely be aware of the Alps as he drives from Paris to Rome. The construction of the Mont Blanc tunnel also marks an important step in the history of civil engineering because, on the French side, new machines are being used which far outdistance, in size and efficiency, anything employed on earlier tunnels. The most important of these is 'Jumbo', a self-propelling engine weighing a hundred tons which runs on rails and can pierce holes twelve feet deep simultaneously with all its fifteen bores. In an hour and a half, 'Jumbo' can drill a hundred and twenty tiny tunnels, hardly big enough for a mouse; but they add up to five hundred and fifty yards of borings ready to be charged with dynamite by the excavators.

477 Machine boring through soft rock (1880).

478 France. Cutting the Mont Blanc tunnel. Six sets of rails have been laid to bring up materials and carry away debris.

The Saint Lawrence Seaway
brings ocean-going vessels to the heart of the Midwest.

Transport and communication is one branch of the contemporary scene which can least afford to grow static; developments in industry, trade and tourism constantly threaten to make the existing facilities out of date or redundant. Several big cities are considering building monorails, like the one which has been running, in solitary splendour, at 479 Wuppertal* in the Ruhr, since 1899—although it has recently been modernised. The Germans fell back on the solution of a monorail because the line between Barmen and Wohwinkel had to cross an over-populated industrial area in which there was simply no land available. The only free space was directly over the River Wupper, so that was where the line had to run. It may well prove a solution to be adopted by other cities suffering from traffic congestion above and below ground.

The highest cable car in Europe is that 480 on the Aiguille du Midi in France*. In less than fifteen minutes it can carry forty passengers from three thousand to thirteen thousand feet. Each of the main cables, slung between the top and bottom stations with no intermediate support, is nearly two miles long.

Perhaps the greatest undertaking in the field of transport in recent years has been the construction of the Saint Lawrence Seaway which makes the Great Lakes of North America—Superior, Michigan, Huron, Erie and Ontario—accessible to ocean-going ships. The opening of the Seaway in 1959, which was performed jointly by Queen Elizabeth II and President Eisenhower as representatives of Canada and the United States, transformed the Great Lakes into a North American equivalent to the Mediterranean. The railway and road transport companies, as well as the Atlantic ports, had held up the project for years without being able to quash it. The U.S.A. and Canada between them invested more than a thousand million dollars in the stepped waterway, with its seven enormous locks. It took four years and twenty-two thousand men to build it. In order 481 to build the system of locks* and canals which would be navigable by even the largest freighters, they dug great canyons, moved whole villages, made an entire new lake, built huge bridges without interrupting the flow of traffic on the river, drained turbulent rapids, and cleared mountainsides of glacial mud and silt.

For the future, Cleveland, Milwaukee, Detroit and Duluth have become sea ports. Iron from Labrador can be carried easily to the steel mills of America. Canadian and American industrialists and exporters have easy access to over six thousand miles of coast. Chicago, already the principal rail and airline centre in North America, is on its way to becoming the first port as well.

479 Germany. Monorail built in 1899 at Wuppertal, in the Ruhr.

480 France. Cable car up the Aiguille du Midi, Haute Savoie.

481 Canada. First lock at the port of Montreal on the Saint Lawrence Seaway. ➤

Modern architecture finds special scope in the construction of airports fit for the present age.

Transcontinental airliners are getting larger, heavier and more powerful all the time. A Douglas DC 8 weighs 141 tons, is 150 feet long and has a wingspan of 140 feet. The aircraft factories in which 482 these airliners are built* are on an even vaster scale than those of the motor industry, and the size of the planes themselves demands enormous working 483 bays. Orly airport*, outside Paris, covers an area of 4,500 acres. It is the most up-to-date in Europe, as large as a town, and contains seven and a half miles of roads; its telephone and drainage installations would be sufficient to supply eight thousand homes. The total weight of the metal structure used in the main building is equal to that of the Eiffel Tower.

484 London Airport*, where twenty-seven thousand employees work for a total of forty-four different companies, is the largest in Europe. But all records for size are beaten by the New York International Airport at Idlewild. This was begun in 1942 and is reserved for intercontinental flights. Although more than three hundred aircraft land there each day, and there are the same number of departures, the airport is still making room for more. 485 One of the six airport buildings*, the building intended to house the larger American companies, has been designed by one of the greatest modern architects: Eero Saarinen. His design has a boldness and freedom which is a tribute to the potentialities of concrete as a building material: the roof is made up of intersecting vaults, supported only at the corners. All the side walls are of glass. The airport as a whole is laid out in the pattern of a gigantic clover leaf, of which the centre is occupied by parking space for six thousand cars and the periphery by airport buildings and runways. There are eleven miles of internal roads; subterranean pipes carry water, electricity, air conditioning and cables. Numerous distinguished architects, engineers and designers collaborated in the designs, under the general direction of Walter K. Harrison, the architect of Rockefeller Center and the United Nations Building.

486 Berlin's Tempelhof Airport* experienced some of its most dramatic moments at the time of the Berlin airlift in 1948. This proved conclusively that large aeroplanes guided by radar could land with perfect safety one after another, every three minutes, at all hours and in any weather, close to a city centre.

483 France. View of Orly Airport, near Paris.

484 England. A Comet outside main building at London Airport.

485 U.S.A. Completion of a building at Idlewild Airport, New York.

486 Germany. Tempelhof Airport during the Berlin airlift of 1948–1949.

◄ 482 U.S.A. Manufacturing Boeings at Seattle, Washington (1959).

487 U.S.S.R. Canal winding through the Kara Kum desert.

489 North Africa. Section of macadam road across the Saha

488 U.S.S.R. Digging the Kara Kum canal.

The population of this planet is already approaching four thousand million and must necessarily cast about for more land to bring under cultivation, and there are indeed still vast stretches of the globe which have never been dug or sown. One of these is the desert which lies to the east of the Caspian Sea, in Turkmenistan and Uzbekistan. Here, up till 1950, the greatest river of central Asia, the Amu Darya, still wound its way through the lunar wastes of Kara Kum. But in this region, as in Kazakhstan, the Russians have embarked upon a programme of land reclamation. Half the waters of the Amu Darya have been diverted to flow away from the Aral Sea into the Caspian, through a section of the bed of the now dried-up River Uzboi. The river wanders

too much to allow the possibility of building a giant dam, which would also have flooded the surrounding oasis. None the less the reservoir at Nukus in Uzbekistan should be sufficient to reduce the amount of water flowing into the Aral Sea, whose level will drop. The 750,000 acres reclaimed by this means are to be transformed into agricultural and pasture land. Other reclamation projects in the Kara Kum desert are being carried out with increasing speed, in the same crusading spirit which has already marked the development of several of Russia's 'hungry steppes'. The first section of the six hundred and fifty-mile canal* took four years to build and demanded a huge labour force which, equipped though it was with only the most primitive tools,

487

still remain to be developed.

aduallly replacing the old caravan trails. Eventually the new road will carry traffic as far south as Tamanrasset.

managed to dig and finish all of two hundred miles. But after that machines 488 appeared on the scene★ and the second section was completed within six months. Villages and agricultural plots grew up one by one along the canal. Once the third section has been finished work can begin on the irrigation ditches which will involve as much effort as the canal itself. Seventeen million acres of land on the shores of the Caspian will be made productive, and Turkmenistan will become a land of oranges and lemons, olive trees and most important of all, cotton. The cultivation of cotton on a large scale can transform the economy of central Asia.

The use of powerful machines for work in desert areas is becoming general as they provide the only adequate solution to the problem of maintaining sufficient human labour on the site for the duration of the work. Although they cannot entirely replace the smaller, lighter machines, these moving giants represent an enormous saving in manpower, in explosives and in motive power.

But before any broader schemes can be undertaken there are certain basic things which have to be done. In the Sahara, for instance, where the recently discovered oil is unlikely to prove its only asset, good, modern tarmac roads are the first essen- 489 tial. The main desert road★ was built at the cost of almost superhuman labour. Lack of water compelled the engineers to resort to an ingenious system of dry cementing, and sandstorms forced them to find a surface material which could stand up to the hottest temperatures and would resist penetration by the finest grains of sand.

Projects are already under consideration, though most are still at an experimental stage, to reclaim much of the desolate waste of the Sahara and make it once again the populous area it was some thousands of years ago. It is hoped to cut a canal through to the port of Gabes, allowing for the passage of barges carrying oil and mineral ores. Already the great trucks, with wheels as high as a man, are beginning to plough up the desert trails. And by tapping water-tables located deep underground it has already been possible to carry out some irrigation work and reclaim good agricultural land from the desert.

The human brain devises
the electronic brain which thinks and calculates more rapidly.

490 U.S.S.R. Dubno. Automatic remote control panel for the synchro-cyclotron.

One man sits at a switchboard covered with hundreds of knobs and dials and controls the innumerable complex and hazardous operations of a great atomic 490 laboratory*. What makes it possible for all these operations to take place without the need for human intervention is electronics. It is electronics that allow all these instruments to run themselves, by 'automation'. It is, moreover, electronics that enabled the instruments to be made in the first place.

Neither the great discoveries of nuclear physics nor the recent achievements in the field of cosmic exploration, with which this book ends, would have been possible without the invention of the electronic brain. The E.N.I.A.C., built in the United States during research on the original atomic bomb, did essential calculations which would have taken ten years if left to the human brain. In 1947 the U.N.I.V.A.C. performed indispensable calculations for the design of the atomic submarine *Nautilus*. Since then electronics have gone from strength to strength. One computer is capable of making sixteen thousand additions or two thousand multiplications per second. Complex electronic circuits ensure the accurate transmission of thousands of 491 messages across vast distances*. Simpler machines can be used to work out salaries, to transmit simultaneous trans- 492 lations at international conferences* and for many other purposes. An electronic 493 coding and programming machine* can regulate the production of an oil refinery, a chemical factory or a foundry; or it can control the operations of a complex 494 marshalling yard*.

491 U.S.A. Automatic telescriptor message centre.

492 U.N.E.S.C.O. Multilingual microphones.

493 France. Punch-card machine. Computer serving to transmit and arrange information in the form of electrical impulses at millisecond speed.

494 France. Section of an important railway marshalling yard at Villeneuve-Saint-Georges, near Paris, which handles eighty trains a day.

As the urban areas become overcrowded, new shopping centres are opened up outside the towns.

Ever since the ancient city of Mohenjo-Daro, urban planning has been a major preoccupation of advanced communities. Technological advances and the development of new building methods continue to give urban development a major place in this history. We can now build faster and higher than ever before. There is lively controversy between partisans of the sprawling, horizontal city, dissected by broad motorways and more suitable to individual homes, and those in favour of vertical cities whose towering apartment blocks are set in green parkland, but require acrobatic feats for ordinary maintenance work*. While cities are crammed 495 to bursting point, the suburban 'shopping centre' is becoming the department store of the space age. The shopping centre developed first in America, where urban congestion reached impossible proportions earlier than elsewhere. The answer was to decentralise, and commercial centres grew up on the edge of towns, or even right out in the country. An area at

least four times that occupied by the shops themselves—already considerable —would be automatically set aside for parking space, as few families would be likely to live within walking distance of the shopping centre; the store indeed relied on its clients' having cars.

Between 1950 and 1960 every town in America was busy building its shopping centre. Next the idea began to spread to South America, as, for instance, to Caracas, and then, even more slowly, to infiltrate into Europe, through England and Sweden. In the evening, after work, thousands of customers drive in to the 496 Northland shopping centre*, near Boston, often with their whole families in roomy 'family' cars, to do their shopping. The centre serves not merely the town but the whole area. There is nothing that cannot be bought there.

Europe, busy rebuilding after the war, played her part in this urban revival. The Interbau Exhibition of 1957 gave Berlin a new district unrivalled anywhere on

495 New York. Cleaning windows of the U.N. Building.

496 U.S.A. Northland Shopping Centre, covering 160 acres, with parking space provided for 7,600 cars.

The functional governs the world.

the continent, and the Brussels Exhibition of 1958 provided a bold new solution for
497 traffic control★. In Milan, three new skyscrapers tower superbly over the city: the thirty-three storey Pirelli building, a four hundred-foot office block for two thousand workers; the glass and duraluminium Galfa building; and the Velasca building, distinguished by a foundation stone ten foot high.

But many of the most enterprising of the new buildings are still to be found in the United States. The Alcoa building in Pittsburgh has a façade thirty floors high completely faced with aluminium. The Lever Building in New York is completely walled in glass. One project with more than a touch of science fiction about it is the proposal by Buckminster Fuller to erect a 'geodesic dome' made of plastic
498 and aluminium★ over the entire centre of New York. Sheltered by such a gigantic, trellised dome Manhattan would become the first city in the world to have a push-button climate.

497 Belgium. Two-level streets at the 1958 Exhibition.

498 New York. Projected geodesic dome made of plastic and aluminium intended to regulate the climate of Manhattan.

277

Brazil builds herself a new capital incorporating all the advances in urban planning.

In its centre of technological studies at Warren in Michigan, General Motors, one of the most powerful single commercial enterprises in the world, has shown the way academic ensembles are likely to develop in the future. Its auditorium consists of an all-aluminium dome, and the low, horizontal lines of the building are given plenty of room in which to expand; the grounds are spacious and graced with an artificial lake★.

499

Other parts of the American continent have their share of futuristic architecture. On the anniversary of the country's discovery by the Portuguese, April 21st, 1960, Brazil celebrated the inauguration of her new capital city: Brasilia★. Brasilia is also the first complete urban building enterprise made possible solely by virtue of aviation. When President Kubitschek's determination finally carried through the decision to build Brasilia on a desert plateau three thousand feet high, the 'Planalto Central' had no connection with any of the coastal areas along which

500

Brazilian cities had previously been concentrated. Machinery and tools of every kind, building materials, and the thousands of workers themselves were brought to the site by an air lift, and the first part of the city to be built was the airport. From there a network of roads was laid out to form the city. The buildings of metal, glass and concrete which go to make up the centre of the city were not merely constructed with an arbitrary determination to let avant garde architects have their fling—although they have been the subject of passionate praises and denunciations the world over—but they are part of the new logic of urban development, rooted nonetheless far back in the past.

The architect Costa marked out the ground with a cross before beginning to build, just as Romulus traced out the limits of the city of Rome. For to the planner the cross means an intersection of roads. One of the two arms of the cross is given over to official and public buildings, while the other arm, curved in the

form of wings seven miles long, is for residential buildings. Banks, offices and amusement buildings are built in terraces round the central axis. This vast concourse, with its superimposed levels of passages and parking spaces, is to lie within the shadow of the cathedral, shaped like an exotic flower, and of the slender mast of the television transmitter. The main central avenue contains three separate lanes, of which the middle one leads to an underground automobile garage. Here at last is a city planned to accommodate all of its road traffic. Away from the centre a belt of individual homes will look onto an artificial lake.

But for many years yet much of these grandiose plans will remain a dream, while the modern pioneers of Brasilia camp in a makeshift city of planks and corrugated iron. It is a bold project, but one that demands long-term financial and technological resources. It can only be carried out successfully with the help of courage and determination.

499 U.S.A. Technological centre of General Motors at Warren, Michigan. Designed by Eero Saarinen.

500 Brazil. Congress Building at Brasilia during construction (1960). ➤

With the perfection of new propulsion fuels, scientists can launch rockets into outer space.

Rockets are not new; they were used by the warriors of Genghiz Khan. But it is only in recent years that they have assumed importance in man's scientific development. In 1890 a Russian, Tsiolkovski, conceived the idea of replacing gunpowder by a liquid fuel for rocket propulsion. In 1935, the American scientist, Goddard, launched a rocket to a height of eight thousand feet. The Germans, in 1944, fired their deadly V2 rockets from a secret launching pad at Peenemunde: missiles capable of carrying a ton of high explosive for a hundred and eighty miles, and consuming ten tons of fuel in under a minute.

After the war the competition between Russia and America to build more effective missiles concentrated chiefly on two objects: to increase the area of total destruction of which their rockets were capable (hence the replacement of existing stocks of high explosive by atomic, and later hydrogen weapons), and to increase their range until they threatened the entire world. The first Russian intercontinental ballistic missile was fired on August 28th, 1957, four months before the American. Testing zones were, for the Russians, from Siberia to the middle of the Pacific Ocean, and for the Americans, from Florida to the area of the South Atlantic beyond Ascension Island. In future no point on the globe would be out of reach of rocket attack.

Peaceful uses have also been found for the rocket. During the 'International Geophysical Year', so called, running from July 1957 to December 1958, the whole world became a laboratory for the most elaborate series of scientific experiments ever carried out. Sixty-seven nations took part. Americans and Russians launched hundreds of rockets to study conditions in space, as a prelude to further explorations.

The first generation of space rockets, 501 such as the Atlas**, weigh a hundred 502 tons, while the newer, more powerful types weigh about forty. The space rockets can travel out beyond the earth's gravity and launch a satellite round the earth, the moon or the sun.

Like a modern sword of Damocles a satellite carrying an H bomb could continue its course without risk in peacetime but at the touch of a button be halted and beamed onto its objective on one of its circuits of the earth—taking only about twenty or thirty minutes. But although this is one military possibility for the use of satellites, there are scientific ends also.

The Russians launched *Sputnik I* into space on October 4th, 1957. Four months later the Americans followed it with *Explorer I*. The space race was on. The Americans launched seventy satellites, some of them still in orbit and sending out radio waves. In January 1959 a Russian projectile weighing a ton became the first artificial satellite to orbit the sun. In October of the same year the Russian *Lunik III* took photographs of the other side of the moon and sent back pictures by television.

502 U.S.A. 'Atlas' Intercontinental ballistic missile on exhibition to the public in 1959. Weight on launching pad: 130 tons. Range: 6,000 miles.

◄ 501 U.S.A. Exhibition model of the Atlas rocket.

503 U.S.A. Mount Palomar Observatory, California. The telescope has a 16 ft. lens.

504 France. Radio-astronomy station at Nançay, Cher. Interferometer antennae.

On the eve of the Second World War it may well have seemed as if the giant telescope at Mount Palomar represented the culminating point in astronomical science.

Its great reflector, made of a special pyrex, fifteen feet in diameter and weighing fourteen tons, was duly packed in protective layers of soft rubber and in November 1947 transported from Pasadena to the top of Mount Palomar in a case whose total weight came to thirty-five tons. It was taken up to the chosen site, 5,500 feet up, by a carefully planned 155-mile route. This telescope*, with its electronic control devices whereby it can keep track of any point in the heavens, making an allowance for the earth's gravitation, was the result of years of research. After two years of intensive optical and mechanical adjustments and of painstaking polishing of the entire surface of the reflector by hand, the first pictures of the sky were taken in 1949, as a result of which the visible universe was extended by two thousand million light-years. It is almost impossible to imagine such a figure, but it corresponds to twelve thousand million billions of miles. The Mount Palomar telescope can 'see' stars, and in particular the groups of stars known as nebulae, at a distance which seems to us to be infinite. Yet it is possible to 'hear' stars even further away from us than this. Jansky was the first to discover, while conducting experiments on sound waves in 1932, that it was possible to bounce Hertzian waves off the Milky Way. Research on ultra-short waves during the Second World War, especially with radar, provided astronomers with instruments capable of capturing radio-electric waves emitted by stars ten thousand million light-years away from earth.

The first observations of radio-astronomy were made using the classical type of antennae or by radar. But even radar waves, the shortest electro-magnetic waves, are fifty thousand times longer than light waves. To obtain the same separative power the antennae of a radio telescope would have to be tens of thousands of times greater than the reflectors of ordinary telescopes: a practical impossibility. Instead, radio-astronomers use a series of interconnected antennae spread out over a base of

mysteries of astronomy.

several miles. When the signals received from interferometers of this type, such 504 as the one at Nançay*, are compared together, they provide information analogous to that which would have been obtained from a single reflector of the same diameter as the base area covered.

However, scientists have succeeded in erecting some giant antennae. The 505 largest of these is at Jodrell Bank* in Cheshire. It consists of a huge concave bowl two hundred and fifty feet in diameter, lined with sheet steel, with a sixty-five-foot antenna in the centre. The steel beams supporting the enormous reflector are attached to a movable chassis running on circular rails, to allow the radio telescope to be turned to face any direction.

An even more powerful radiotelescope is being constructed at Nançay. This consists of two groups of facing reflectors, set in fine metal grilles, proof against the effects of temperature and wind pressure. The first of these reflector-antennae, which is three hundred and thirty yards long and as tall as a ten-storey building, turns against the rotation of the earth, and as it captures interstellar rays, reflects them onto a second, curved reflector with a radius of six hundred and fifty yards and a surface area of twelve thousand square yards. From this single reflector, waves travel to the observation chamber.

In the whole of the solar system (apart from the sun itself), only the lunar sun gives off measurable rays. This has made it possible to prove that the surface of the moon is covered with a layer of fine dust, a few millimetres thick, resting on a bed of porous rock. This is only one of the minor discoveries about the nature of extra-terrestrial matter which we owe to radio-astronomy, but it is already an invaluable piece of information, perhaps, for the cosmonauts of the future.

Similar antennae can be used to detect waves coming from our own planet with astonishing accuracy. By means of a vast 506 network of radar early warning screens* circling the Arctic, and running from Iraq to the Baltic, the United States are able to keep as close a watch on Russia as Jodrell Bank does on the heavens. To guard against possible rocket attacks across the Arctic, Canada has built a radio-electric Great Wall of China right across her northern frontiers.

505 Great Britain. Jodrell Bank radiotelescope (diameter: 250 ft.).

506 Canada. Early warning screens extending from British Columbia to Labrador.

The space rockets are more than an invention;
they are an epic. Their heroes are the astronauts.

507 U.S.A. 'Titan' rocket under construction. Measurements: 90 ft. long and 10 ft. broad at the base.

508 U.S.A. Project Mercury. Ejection of capsule.

509 U.S.S.R. Major Yuri Gagarin about to enter the space ship *Vostok*.

510 U.S.A. Testing human reactions to conditions inside a space capsule (Project Mercury).

507 Rockets grew more ambitious*, but it still remained to be seen whether man could live in space. As a first step the Russians sent up two dogs, Strelka and Belka, in August 1960. They were recovered in good condition and were followed, in January 1961, by the American chimpanzee, Ham. One object

508 of the American Project Mercury* space programme was to reduce all the essential components to the smallest, most compact dimensions, whereas the Russian scientists were putting space capsules of many tons into orbit. The first orbit of the moon was made by a Russian rocket.

On April 12th, 1961, the Russians launched the first man into space.

509 Major Yuri Gagarin*, in the *Vostok*, made one circuit of the earth in a hundred and eight minutes, at a speed of 17,500 m.p.h. and landed safe and sound. On May 5th the first American astronaut, Commander Alan Shepard succeeded in travelling some distance outside the earth's atmosphere aboard a *Mercury*

510 capsule*. Colonel Glenn stayed up for three orbits in February 1962; six months before that, however, Major Titov had already completed seventeen successive orbits round the earth.

The curiosity of man is without limits.

Once he has explored the earth, he must turn his attention to other planets.

511 U.S.S.R. The Russian astrophysicist Tsiolkovsky's conception of an interplanetary station.

513 U.S.A. Atomic flying saucers.

512 U.S.S.R. Leningrad. Studio shot of a science fiction film.

The complexity of these space rockets and the laboratories and workshops where they are made is brought sharply home by the fact that each rocket contains over thirty-six thousand parts, made and finished in hundreds of special laboratories. The radio-control system alone contains twelve thousand parts. The object of this fantastic undertaking is to lead man to the exploration of other planets. It is a realm in which fact and theory are close together and fact frequently turns out stranger than fiction.

The Americans already have plans for the *Nova* rocket, a two hundred and fifty-foot monster, three times as tall as *Atlas*, capable of lifting a giant satellite weighing nine tons. But even before *Nova* starts to be built it may be surpassed by other smaller rockets powered by new and amazingly powerful fuels. At any rate at this stage the permanent space station*, assembled actually in space, rather than on the ground, from parts carried up by rocket ships, does not seem altogether an impossibility. Such stations could act as laboratories for studying the effect of prolonged weightlessness on human beings and for observing meteorites and levels of

511

514 U.S.A. 100 ft. sphere of the type used for the 'Echo' satellite balloon. Langley, Virginia.

radiation. But they could also provide intermediate stations on the way to distant planets, such as Mars, and observation and control stations for things happening on earth.

Our own satellite, the moon, is a natural target for exploration, and because little is known of Soviet plans in this connection all forecasts seem pure guesswork. Soviet 512 film-makers*, however, have already taken an advance look at the first men on the moon that does not strike one as unduly fanciful. What does look more like 513 science fiction is the flying saucer* powered by atomic energy, serving to transport passengers, freight and mail.

It is true that there are already many achievements in the field of space exploration which are as exciting as anything in fiction. In August 1960 the 514 'Echo' balloon* was sent up to a height of a thousand miles above the earth's surface. A chemical powder inside the folded balloon then reacted to the sun's heat and filled the balloon with gas until it was as big as a twelve-storey building. A satellite of this type is able to reflect television and radio waves back onto the earth.

The satellite *Transit II* carries an electronic clock to guide atomic submarines. *Tiros* relays meteorological information: it carries two small television cameras which have sent back twenty-three thousand pictures of the earth and its blanket of clouds in the space of four months. *Courrier IB* carries radio and telegraphic equipment able to pick up 773,693 words in fourteen minutes and transmit them in a few seconds to another distant station.

Will the fantastic developments of the space age reduce the great works of mankind to a simple matter of pushing 515 buttons? No, the space capsule*, with the vast accumulation of scientific knowledge which lies behind it, is, like all the previous inventions recorded in these pages, simply a further stage in man's discovery of the properties of the world in which he lives. However far he may travel among the stars, man's home, and his workshop, is still the earth. It is to be hoped that as the human race gains increasing power over nature, it will cultivate a corresponding measure of responsibility in the use to which it puts its new acquisitions.

515 U.S.A. Space capsule with retro-rockets and floats.

Photo Credits

Photographs not listed come from the archives of Editions du Pont Royal, Paris.

a

b

c

d

e

Table of Contents

CHAPTER IV

ISFAHAN AND VERSAILLES
The Monarchs as Builders

CHAPTER V

SUEZ AND MANHATTAN
The New Iron Age

CHAPTER VI

RIO AND DNIEPROGES
The Age of Confidence

CHAPTER VII

ESSEN AND AN SHAN
All the World a Workshop

CHAPTER VIII

OAK RIDGE AND VOSTOK
From the Atom to the Cosmos

N° d'éditeur : 29